When Eddie Wilson's friends all began to take music lessons, Eddie didn't know what to make of it. It wasn't that he didn't like music, but since he could hear it on the radio and television, he saw no reason why he should make music himself. He listened to his friend Sidney sawing away on her cello next door and thought it sounded like a dying cow. But as one child after another earned a place in the school's new orchestra, Eddie began to have a change of heart. Then one morning, as he was singing in the bathtub, he suddenly became enchanted with the sound of his own voice. He felt as if he could keep on singing forever. The only trouble was that Eddie's three brothers wanted to get into the bathroom.

EDDIE MAKES MUSIC

By the Same Author

EDDIE'S GREEN THUMB. 1964
HERE COMES THE BUS! 1963
SNOWBOUND WITH BETSY. 1962
ANNIE PAT AND EDDIE. 1960
EDDIE AND LOUELLA. 1959
BETSY'S WINTERHOUSE. 1958
EDDIE MAKES MUSIC. 1957
BETSY'S BUSY SUMMER. 1956
EDDIE AND HIS BIG DEALS. 1955
BETSY AND THE CIRCUS. 1954
EDDIE'S PAY DIRT. 1953
THE MIXED-UP TWINS. 1952
EDDIE AND GARDENIA. 1951
BETSY'S LITTLE STAR. 1950
EDDIE AND THE FIRE ENGINE. 1949
PENNY GOES TO CAMP. 1948
LITTLE EDDIE. 1947

Published by William Morrow and Company

PENNY AND PETER. 1946
BETSY AND THE BOYS. 1945
HERE'S A PENNY. 1944
BACK TO SCHOOL WITH BETSY. 1943
PRIMROSE DAY. 1942
BETSY AND BILLY. 1941
TWO AND TWO ARE FOUR. 1940
"B" IS FOR BETSY. 1939

Published by Harcourt, Brace and World

EDDIE

MAKES MUSIC

Written and Illustrated by

CAROLYN HAYWOOD

WILLIAM MORROW AND COMPANY, *New York, 1957*

Seventh Printing, March 1967

Library of Congress Catalog Card No. 57-9111

To Lee and Philip Eckel
this book is lovingly dedicated

CONTENTS

EDDIE MAKES MUSIC

CHAPTER I

SIDNEY PLAYS THE CELLO

Eddie Wilson and Sidney Stewart lived next door to each other. They were also in the same room in school, and they shared many interests. For one thing, they were both collectors. Eddie called his collection "valuable property," while Sidney always spoke of hers as "my treasures." Their parents called both collections "junk."

Eddie had been thrilled when Sidney first moved into the house next door, because Sid seemed to like everything he liked. But Eddie soon discovered that there was one interest that they did not have in common. It was music. Sidney played the cello.

It wasn't that Eddie didn't like music. He liked the record player and some of the music he heard over the radio and television, but as long as somebody else was willing to make music, Eddie saw no reason why he should try to make it himself. He listened to Sidney sawing away on her cello. As the sounds floated out through the window, Eddie thought it sounded like an old cow.

"You should see that thing that Sidney plays, Mama!" Eddie said to his mother, after he had seen the cello for the first time. "It's like a violin, but it's so big she has to stand it on the floor. Then she has to straddle it, like riding a horse."

"Now, Eddie, you know she doesn't sit on her cello!" said his mother.

"Well, no. She sits on a chair, but she has to put her legs around it," said Eddie.

"The cello is a very beautiful instrument, Eddie," said his mother. "One of the most beautiful."

"Maybe Sid doesn't know how to play it," said Eddie.

"She is doing very well," replied his mother. "I hear that she's going to play in a quartet at school."

"What's a quartet?" Eddie asked.

"Four musicians playing together," said his mother. "Two violins, a cello, and a piano are sometimes in a quartet."

"Oh!" said Eddie.

"I think it's about time you learned to play something, Eddie," said his mother.

"Oh, no!" said Eddie. "I don't want to play anything but ball, Mama. I wouldn't be any good at making music. You have to have long fingers, and look at my fingers." Eddie held up his hands. "See how stubby they are."

"They don't look stubby to me," said his mother, "but I don't intend to spend money for music lessons if you are not interested."

"That's right, Mama," said Eddie. "Sid says her father spends a heap of money for her music lessons."

Eddie picked up his football and went out to play. He was glad that he had gotten out of having music lessons so easily.

The following morning, when Eddie left the house to go to school, he saw Sidney coming out of her front door. She was carrying her cello. "Hi, Sid!" Eddie called. "What are you doing with your cello?"

"I'm taking it to school," said Sidney. "We're going to have a rehearsal for our concert."

"That cello looks pretty neat," said Eddie. "Nice plaid overcoat you have on it."

"Overcoat!" exclaimed Sidney. "That's a case! Mother is driving me to school. Want to come along?"

"Oh, sure!" said Eddie. "Thanks! Can I help you put the cello into the car?"

"You can open the back door," said Sidney. "I never let anybody touch my cello."

Eddie opened the door, and Sidney placed the cello on the back seat. Then she climbed into the front seat of the car. Just then Mrs. Stewart came out of the house, jingling her car keys. "Good morning, Eddie," she said. "Hop in."

"Good morning," replied Eddie, and he jumped into the front seat beside Sidney. "Who else is going to play?" he asked, as they started off.

"Oh, Margie Clark plays the piano and Davy Hawkins plays the violin," replied Sidney.

"Davy Hawkins plays the violin!" exclaimed Eddie. "The poor fish! I guess that's why he never turns up on the ball lot. I guess he has to practice all the time."

"But, Eddie," said Sidney, "when you make lovely music, you don't mind practicing."

"I would," said Eddie. "Glad I'm not musical. Who

else is in this, uh, what do you call it—pint something? No, quart something."

"Quartet!" said Sidney.

"Yes, quartet," said Eddie. "Who else is in it?"

"Rosalie Roberts," said Sidney. "Kenny's sister."

"That little thing!" exclaimed Eddie.

"She may be little, but she plays the violin very well," said Sidney. "We'd like to have a vocalist with our quartet," she added.

"A what?" said Eddie.

"A vocalist," said Sidney. "You know, they have them on TV. Don't you know what a vocalist is?"

"No. What is one?" said Eddie.

"Why, somebody who sings," said Sidney.

"Oh!" said Eddie. "I thought they were called crooners."

Suddenly the car began to bump. "Oh, dear!" exclaimed Mrs. Stewart. "I believe I have a flat tire."

"Oh, Mother!" cried Sidney. "I can't be late for school. First thing is the rehearsal."

"You'll have to walk the rest of the way," said her mother.

"You mean, carry the cello?" exclaimed Sidney.

"There's nothing else to do," said her mother. "By the time they come from the service station and change this tire, you'll be late. You can do it. Just be careful."

Sidney opened the car door, and the two children climbed out. Mrs. Stewart got out too. She opened the back door and lifted the cello out. She handed it to Sidney.

"I'd carry it for you, Sid," said Eddie, "but I know you never let anybody touch your cello."

"Oh, I can carry it," said Sidney. "I like to carry it. Could you carry my books and my music portfolio?"

"Sure!" said Eddie, taking Sidney's books and portfolio.

The children called good-by to Mrs. Stewart and started off. Soon their way led up a long, steep hill. Sidney began to puff.

"Better go into second gear, Sid," said Eddie.

Sidney stood still. She rested the end of the cello on the sidewalk. "Eddie," she said, "if you will be very, very careful, I'll let you carry my cello, as a very special favor."

"Oh, no, Sid!" said Eddie. "I think you'd better not trust me with your cello. You know I'm awful clumsy. I might fall down and smash that cello all to bits. Just take it slowly. Hold your head up and breathe real deep."

Sidney shifted the cello and started off again. She held her head up and breathed real deep.

"Atta girl!" said Eddie. "You got the idea."

"But if I hold my head up, I can't see where I am walking," said Sidney.

"Just keep walking, Sid," said Eddie. "I'll do the looking. Careful there, don't step on that broken brick." Sid missed the broken brick. "Hey, mind that chewing gum! Big wad of it right in front of you. Oh, you stepped right in it. Bet it's stuck to your shoe. Hold up your foot."

Sidney managed to hold up her foot and her cello at the same time.

"Yep! You got it on your shoe, all right," said Eddie.

"Well, take it off," said Sidney. "I don't want chewing gum all over my shoe."

"Oh, you'll walk it off," said Eddie. "I haven't anything to take it off with."

Sidney hoisted up the cello again, and the children went on.

"Just keep your head up," said Eddie. "Breathe deep. I learned that at the Scouts'. I'll watch where you're going. Oops! Careful of that piece of wire. Don't get it tangled around your leg."

Sidney missed the piece of wire by an inch.

"Careful! Careful!" Eddie sang out in another minute. "Don't step on that! Somebody must have broken a bottle of mustard."

Sidney looked down and missed the mustard by an eyelash.

"You're doing fine!" said Eddie. "Keep your head up."

"I'll be glad when I get to school," said Sidney. "I wish our school wasn't on top of a hill."

"I'm glad I'm not musical," said Eddie. Then he gave a sudden cry. "Well, what do you think of that! Am I lucky! There's a dime right in the middle of the pavement!"

Eddie stooped down and picked up the dime.

Sidney stopped. She rested the end of the cello on the pavement again. "Eddie Wilson!" said Sidney. "You never would have seen that dime if you hadn't been looking at the pavement for me. If you hadn't told me to keep my head up, I would have found it. So it is really mine."

"Yours!" cried Eddie. "You never even saw it."

"How could I see it when I had my head up?" said Sidney. "You let me pick up chewing gum on my best shoes, but when I come to a dime you pick it up."

"Say!" cried Eddie. "If I hadn't been with you, you

24

would have tripped over the broken brick, got your shoes full of mustard, and tangled your feet up in that piece of wire. It's worth a dime to get you to school with that cello. Am I glad I'm not musical!"

Tears came into Sidney's eyes. "Eddie Wilson!" she cried. "I think you're mean. I think you ought to let me carry those things and you carry the cello a little while."

"Okay!" said Eddie, putting the books and the portfolio down.

"Now do be careful!" Sidney said, as she handed the cello to Eddie. "Don't drop it, and be careful not to kick it, and don't fall."

"Okay! Okay!" said Eddie.

"Keep your head up and breathe deep," said Sidney. "And don't trip."

At the next corner, halfway up the hill, they met Boodles Cary and Dumpty Peterson. They were great chums of Eddie's.

"What you got there, Eddie?" Dumpty called out.

"It's a cello," said Sidney.

"What's it for?" said Boodles.

"You make music with it," said Eddie. "Do you want to carry it?"

"Nope," said Boodles. "I didn't know you could play a thing like that, Eddie."

"He can't," said Sidney. "It's mine. I play it."

"Wait until you hear her," said Eddie. "It sounds like a dying cow."

"Eddie Wilson, it does not!" said Sidney. "My teacher says that I play very well for my age."

"Well, say!" said Dumpty. "Are you going to carry it to school every day?"

"If she does," said Eddie, "I'll ask my father to move."

"Of course not!" said Sidney. "We have a rehearsal today. It's our quartet. My mother had a flat tire. Keep your head up, Eddie. Breathe deep."

"What does he have to breathe deep for?" said Dumpty, as he and Boodles fell into step with Sidney and Eddie.

"So he doesn't get winded, carrying the cello up the hill," said Sidney.

"I found a dime," said Eddie. "Picked it up right on the sidewalk."

"You did!" exclaimed Boodles.

"You sure are lucky!" said Dumpty. "You always find things."

"It wasn't fair," said Sidney. "Eddie told me to keep my head up and he would watch where I was walking, and he let me step in the chewing gum, but when he saw a dime he picked it up."

"Well, you didn't expect me to pick up the old chewing gum, did you?" said Eddie.

"Of course not!" said Sidney. "But if I'd been looking, I wouldn't have stepped in the chewing gum and I would have had the dime."

"Yeah, and you would have dropped your old cello picking it up," said Eddie.

They were still arguing about the dime when they reached school.

"I'm glad I never got mixed up with music," said Eddie, as he handed the cello to Sidney.

"Me too," said Dumpty.

When Sidney walked into the classroom with her cello, there was a great deal of excitement, especially among the girls.

"Oh, I think it would be wonderful to play the cello!" said Debbie.

"I'd like to play the harp," said Anna Patricia. "I think I'll ask my mother to let me get a harp and take lessons. You look so beautiful when you play the harp. Just like an angel."

As soon as the bell rang, Miss Rice, the teacher, said, "The members of the quartet are excused for rehearsal."

Sidney, Rosalie, and Davy picked up their instruments. Margie picked up her portfolio of music. Polly, with nothing but her handkerchief, followed the four musicians out of the door.

"What's Polly going to play?" Eddie asked.

"Polly is going to turn the music for Margie," replied Miss Rice.

"She gets out of arithmetic just to turn pages?" said Eddie. "I could do that!"

"No, you couldn't, Eddie," said Miss Rice. "You have to be able to read the notes."

"Oh!" said Eddie. "I guess you have to be musical."

"That's right," said Miss Rice. "And now I have a very important announcement to make. This school is going to have an orchestra. We find that there are quite a number of children in our school who can play musical instruments, and Mr. Saunders, who is training the quartet, will be here every Monday to train our orchestra. Any boys and girls in this room who can play instruments are to meet with Mr. Saunders as soon as the members of the quartet return."

The children looked delighted at the idea of having a school orchestra.

"Now!" said Miss Rice. "How many children in this room play a musical instrument?"

A number of hands were raised, including Eddie's.

Miss Rice nodded to Katherine. "Katherine," she said, "what do you play?"

"I'm taking violin lessons," she replied.

"Good!" said Miss Rice. "Fred, what do you play?"

"I can play the trumpet," he answered.

"Fine," said his teacher. "Walter, what about you?"

"My father said he would get me a clarinet," replied Walter.

"Can you play a clarinet?" Miss Rice asked.

"Not yet," replied Walter.

"Well, you had better get it and learn to play it, and you can be in the orchestra," said Miss Rice.

"What's a clarinet, Miss Rice?" Boodles asked.

"It is a kind of instrument," replied their teacher. "It's one of the wood-wind instruments."

Eddie's hand was still up. "And what do you play, Eddie?" Miss Rice asked.

"My brother Rudy has a sweet potato," said Eddie. "I could learn to play that."

"I'm sorry, Eddie, but there will not be any sweet potatoes in our orchestra," said his teacher. "Now let's get down to our arithmetic lesson."

When the children from the quartet returned, Miss Rice said, "Now the boys and girls who play instruments are to go to the auditorium."

"If you play the piano, do you go?" asked Ruth.

"Yes, if you play the piano, go," replied Miss Rice.

Six children left the room. Eddie watched them go with a feeling of disappointment. He felt left out, and he didn't like feeling left out. Eddie liked to be in on things, not left behind.

That afternoon when Eddie arrived home from school, he said to his mother, "Mama, I want to play something!"

His mother looked at him in surprise and said, "Go play football."

"I don't mean that kind of playing," said Eddie. "I mean I want to play a horn or something."

"Why, Eddie!" exclaimed his mother. "You told me,

only yesterday, that you didn't want to play anything but ball."

"Well, I've changed my mind," said Eddie. "I'm going to be musical."

"Then there must be a reason," said his mother.

Eddie grinned at her. "Sure," he said. "Our school is going to have an orchestra."

"And you want to be in the orchestra," said his mother, laughing.

"That's right," said Eddie.

Just then he caught sight of Sidney returning from a music lesson. Eddie ran out of the front door. "Hi, Sid!" he called.

Sidney stood still and waited for Eddie. Then he stuck his hand in his pocket and pulled out a little paper bag. "I spent that dime for a candy bar," he said. "Here! I saved this half for you."

"Oh, Eddie! Thanks!" said Sidney. "You're swell."

"Oh, that's okay," replied Eddie. "And, by the way, I'm musical too now."

"What are you going to play?" Sidney asked.

"I don't know yet," said Eddie. "Something easy, 'cause I have to learn fast and get into that orchestra."

CHAPTER II

SHOPPING FOR WIND INSTRUMENTS

WHEN Eddie's brothers, Joe and Frank, came home from school, they rushed into the kitchen to make themselves peanut-butter sandwiches. Joe and Frank were twins. They were older than Eddie, but they still went to the same school he did. Rudy, the eldest of the Wilson boys, was in junior high.

34

"Hi!" said Eddie, as he joined the twins and helped himself to a slice of bread. "Did you hear the news?"

"What news?" said Joe.

"About the orchestra," replied Eddie, spreading peanut butter on his bread. "Pass the jelly."

Frank passed the jelly.

"I'm going to be in it," said Eddie.

"You?" exclaimed Frank. "What can you play?"

"Nothing yet," replied Eddie. "But it's not going to be the violin, because the violin is hard. You have to saw across the strings with one hand and wiggle your fingers up and down the strings with the other. That's hard. I'm going to play a horn. All you have to do is blow." Eddie sank his teeth into his sandwich.

"Eddie, you don't know what you're talking about," said Frank. "You have to blow and push little keys as well. Joe and I have just decided, walking home from school, that we're going to be in the orchestra. We're going to play horns. You're too little to play a horn. You couldn't blow hard enough."

"I could so," said Eddie. "I know I could."

At dinner that evening Eddie said to his father, "Dad, we're going to have an orchestra at our school."

"Fine!" said his father. "I suppose Sidney will be playing her cello in the orchestra."

"Oh, sure!" said Eddie. "And I'm going to play the horn."

"He is not," said Frank. "Joe and I are going to play horns. Eddie's too little."

Rudy looked up from his plate. "What do you know about that!" he exclaimed. "The fellow in our school orchestra who plays the drums is going to school in Switzerland for six months, and he said that I could keep his drums for him and learn to play them. I'm going to get them today."

"Dad!" said Eddie. "I can so learn to play the horn, can't I?"

"Where are all these horns coming from?" asked his father.

"I thought you would buy a horn for me," said Eddie.

"Don't you want me to be musical? Mama wants me to be musical."

"I don't think we could stand it," replied his father, "with Sidney next door practicing on that cello, Rudy beating on the drums, and the rest of you blowing horns. But whether we could or not, I am not spending any money on horns. How do you know that you would be any good at it?"

The three boys looked very glum.

"Do you know what horns cost?" asked their father.

"I wish you wouldn't all call them horns," said Rudy. "They are wind instruments."

"All right, wind instruments," said his father. "Do you know what a wind instrument costs, Eddie?"

"A couple of dollars, I guess," said Eddie.

"A couple of dollars!" exclaimed his father. "They cost over a hundred dollars."

"Over a hundred dollars!" cried Eddie, Joe, and Frank in a chorus.

"Yes, indeed," said Mr. Wilson. "If you boys want

these things, you'll have to find a way to earn the money to buy them."

"It takes a long time to earn a hundred dollars," said Joe.

"Indeed it does," replied his father.

"Maybe I can get one in a secondhand store," said Eddie.

"That's a good idea!" exclaimed Frank. And turning to his twin, he said, "Let's try the secondhand stores, Joe."

"I thought of it first," said Eddie. "Now you want to go out and buy up the horns."

"You don't mean that all the secondhand stores in this town are your private property, do you?" exclaimed Joe.

"Well, if there's a secondhand horn in this town, I'm going to get it," said Eddie.

The following day was Saturday, and Eddie was up bright and early. At half past eight, when Eddie rode off on his bicycle, the twins were still sound asleep. He

was on his way to the secondhand stores with all of the money he owned—four dollars and eighty-three cents.

He arrived at the first one before it was open, so he had plenty of time to look in the window. The window contained many things that Eddie would have been delighted to own, but he didn't see a horn of any kind. This, however, did not discourage him. The store was large, and he could see through the glass in the door that it was piled high with lots of different things. Surely somewhere there would be a horn. Any kind of a horn will do, thought Eddie. As long as it makes a noise when you blow it, it will be all right.

Eddie had been peering into the store about fifteen minutes when the storekeeper came to open the door. "Well, young fella, what can I do for you?" he asked.

"Have you got any horns?" Eddie asked.

"Sure, sure!" said the man. "I got a beautiful coat rack made of horns off a deer—beautiful! Sell it to you cheap."

"No," said Eddie. "I don't want a coat rack."

"Well, you can take the horns off the coat rack," said the man. "They come off easy."

"I want a horn that you blow," said Eddie. "A musical instrument."

"Oh!" said the man. "You want a musical instrument." He stood thinking for a moment. Suddenly he said, "You want a good musical instrument? I got the very thing. I got a musical instrument you'll be crazy about. I give it to you at a big bargain, 'cause you're my first customer today. Anybody else, I charge 'em double. You just come back and look at this musical instrument."

Eddie followed the man into the back of the store. Here the storekeeper began moving little tables, chairs, lamps, jugs and jars of all sizes, and parts of things that had broken, so that Eddie couldn't tell what they had been. Finally, from out of a big old refrigerator, the shopkeeper brought out something that looked like a large box on one leg. It had a crank handle on one side of it.

42

"There!" cried the shopkeeper. "There is a musical instrument! Better than a horn, hey?"

"But I want a horn," said Eddie. "Not a hand organ."

"Why do you want a horn when you can get this?" asked the man. "Listen!" He began to grind the handle. A tinny sound came forth. Eddie recognized the tune. It was *The Band Played On*. "Beautiful!" said the man.

"I want a horn," said Eddie.

"Look!" said the shopkeeper. "Say you get a horn. What then? You have to take lessons. You have to blow and blow and blow, and it comes out sour, like pickles. You have to learn to read the notes on the sheet of music. All those little black dots running all over the page. You have to practice every day after school, and at the end of two months what can you play? Not even *Yankee Doodle!* What do you have to do to play this musical instrument? Just hang it around your neck!" The man hung the hand organ around Eddie's neck by an old leather strap. The strap broke, and the organ fell on the floor. The man picked it up. "Don't worry

43

about that," he said. "Can be fixed easy. Hold it here by the leg. Now crank it."

Eddie held it by the leg, which was now very wobbly. He cranked it. Now it played *A Bicycle Built for Two.* Dust came out with the music.

"See how easy it is to make music?" said the man. "It's a bargain. How much money do you have?"

"Four dollars and eighty-three cents," said Eddie.

"Okay!" said the man. "It's worth twice that much, but I let you have it for four dollars and eighty-three cents."

"I want a horn," said Eddie, handing the organ back to the man.

"Okay!" said the man. "But when you're blowing your lungs out, you'll be sorry you didn't buy this organ."

Eddie walked out of the store, climbed on his bike, and rode off.

Back at the Wilsons', the twins were about to leave to hunt for their musical instruments. "Let's each go by himself," said Joe, "and see what there is. No use both of us going into every store. Then we'll meet back here at lunch time and see what we have turned up."

"That's a good idea," said Frank. The boys climbed on their bicycles and rode off in opposite directions.

Soon Frank arrived at the store where Eddie had been. When he walked into the dark shop from the bright sunshine, it was several minutes before he could see all the things piled around the walls.

"Well, young fella," said the shopkeeper, walking toward him from the rear of the store, "what can I do for you?"

"Have you any wind instruments?" said Frank.

"Wind instruments?" the man repeated. "Sure! Sure!" He led the way to the back of the store. "Got a couple someplace back here."

Once again he moved the tables and chairs, and the jugs and the jars until he came to a pile of old curtains. Underneath the pile of curtains he found what he was looking for. He picked it up and set it on the floor in

45

front of Frank. "There you are, young man," he said. "Best wind instrument you can buy. Give you a good bargain."

Frank looked down at the wind instrument. It was an old electric fan. "Oh, no!" said Frank. "What I want is a musical instrument."

"Oh!" said the shopkeeper. "A musical instrument. I thought you said a wind instrument. Oh, I have a musical instrument. You'll be crazy about it. It's in the window. Fella was just in looking at it. Now if he comes back, it's sold. Well, that's the way it goes. Pass up a bargain and the next fella gets it."

Frank followed the shopkeeper to the front of the store. The man opened the back of the window and lifted the hand organ out. "There you are!" he said. "Strap needs a little repairing. Let me play it for you."

The shopkeeper rested the organ on its wobbly leg. The leg immediately fell off. If he hadn't been holding on to the handle, the organ would have fallen on the floor for the second time that morning. "Little glue

46

will fix that," said the man. "I'll give you a big bargain." He set the organ on a nearby table and turned the crank. Once more *The Band Played On* wheezed and squeaked through the shop. "Beautiful, hey?" said the man.

"Not for me!" said Frank. "I want a trumpet."

"Say, young fella, why don't you say what you want? First you want a wind instrument. Then you want a musical instrument. Now you want a trumpet. This is a lot easier to play."

"No," said Frank. "I want a trumpet."

"Okay! Okay!" said the man. "But you're making a mistake."

Frank went out of the store and hopped on his bike. Off he went down the street.

In the meantime Joe was in another secondhand store, asking for a trumpet. "I'm sorry, son," said the shopkeeper. "I had a trumpet this morning, but I sold it. Boy came in 'bout an hour ago. Said his school was going to have an orchestra. He wanted a trumpet."

"I'll bet that was my little brother Eddie!" said Joe. "Was he a little fellow?"

"That's right!" said the man. "Little fellow, 'bout so high." The man held his hand out, level with Joe's shoulder.

"That's Eddie, I'll bet!" said Joe. "That kid gets everything!"

"Well now," said the man, "I have a nice trombone here." He lifted a case off a shelf and opened it up. Inside lay the trombone.

Joe looked at it with great interest, for it was in three parts. There was the trumpet section, a double-rod section, and the mouthpiece. "How much is it?" he asked.

"You can have this trombone for thirty dollars," said the man.

"Oh! I only have eight dollars," said Joe.

"I'm sorry, son," said the shopkeeper, "but you'll never get an instrument for eight dollars. This is very cheap at thirty."

Joe looked sad. Then suddenly his face brightened. "How much was the trumpet?" he asked.

"I sold that for twenty-five dollars," replied the man.

"Then you didn't sell it to my brother Eddie!" said Joe. "He never had twenty-five dollars to spend."

"Don't know who he was," said the man. "Didn't give his name."

"Must be a millionaire," said Joe, as he walked out of the shop.

About fifteen minutes later Joe reached the shop where the hand organ was. It was still sitting on the counter. "Hello!" said the shopkeeper when he saw Joe. "So you're back! Back for that organ, I guess."

"I wasn't here before," said Joe. "I guess my twin brother was here."

"Sure do look alike," said the man. "What can I do for you?"

"Did my brother find any kind of a wind instrument here?" asked Joe.

"He didn't get a trumpet, if that's what you mean,"

said the man. "But if you're looking for a good musical instrument, I've got one."

Once again the shopkeeper picked up the old hand organ. "Strap needs a little repairing, and a spot of glue will fix this leg. Be as good as new then." He took hold of the handle and gave one crank. Off came the handle. The man looked at it carefully. "Oh, easy fixed," he said. "I'll give you a big reduction. It plays beautifully. Too bad you can't hear it. But you take my word. I give you a big bargain."

"No thanks," said Joe. "I'm hunting for a wind instrument."

When the boys turned up for lunch, Joe was the only one who had found a wind instrument. He told them about the trombone that cost thirty dollars.

"Thirty dollars!" exclaimed Frank.

"He said he sold a trumpet to a fella from our school for twenty-five dollars this morning," said Joe.

"Why, even if we put our money together, we wouldn't have enough," said Frank.

"How much do you have?" asked Joe.

"Seven dollars," replied Frank.

"That would be fifteen," said Joe. "That is only half of thirty." Then he looked over at Eddie, who was eating his soup. "How much do you have, Eddie?" he asked.

"I'm not going to chip in for your horn," said Eddie. "What good would it do me?"

"You could take lessons on it," said Joe.

"What good would it do me to take lessons if I didn't have a horn to play in the orchestra?" said Eddie. "I would be wasting all my breath."

Joe leaned over and whispered to Frank. "Let's ask Mother if she will lend us fifteen dollars. That would only be a seven-fifty loan to each of us."

"But what good is one trombone?" asked Frank, helping himself to a piece of cake.

"It's in three pieces," said Joe. "You can have one piece, and I can have the other, and we can lend the third piece to Eddie."

"You're crazy, Joe," said Frank. "You have to put it together to play it."

"Okay!" said Joe. "But one trombone is better than none, isn't it? We could start learning anyway."

"Well, yes," said Frank. "Let's ask Mother as soon as she comes home from town." He looked up at the clock. "She said she would be home at two o'clock."

It wasn't long before they heard their mother come into the house. Before she had her hat off, they had told her about the trombone. "If you would lend us each seven fifty," said Frank, "we'd be able to buy it and start taking lessons."

"How would you pay me back?" asked their mother.

"We can earn it," said Joe. "We can cut grass and rake leaves, and in the winter we can shovel snow."

"Looks as though I'm going to have to wait a long time for my fifteen dollars," said Mother.

"We'll pay you interest on it," said Frank.

"Never mind the interest," said Mother. "Just return the fifteen dollars."

"You mean you're going to lend it to us?" said **Joe.**

"Yes, I'll lend it to you," said their mother.

"That's wonderful!" said Frank.

"Oh, yes, Mother! Thanks! We'll practice, won't we, Frank?" said Joe.

Soon the twins had the thirty dollars. As they left the house, their mother called after them, "Tell the man that if it's not a good trombone, your father will take it back to him."

"Okay!" the twins called back.

This time Eddie went with them. They rode their bicycles as fast as they could. When they hopped off of them in front of the store, Joe said, "I hope nobody else bought it."

"Wouldn't that be awful?" said Frank, and the twins rushed into the store, followed by Eddie.

"We have the thirty dollars for the trombone," Joe called out.

"Yes, we have the thirty dollars," said Frank.

"Then it's yours," said the shopkeeper. He took the

trombone out of the case and said, "Now I'll show you boys how to put this together. You have to do it carefully, you know."

"My mother said I should tell you that if it isn't a good trombone, my father will bring it back," said Joe.

"Okay!" said the man. "But I know it *is* a good one. I'll blow it for you, and you can see for yourselves." The shopkeeper put the trombone to his lips and blew a deep blast. "Good tone," he said. "I'll take it into the back shop and polish it up a bit."

When he brought the trombone back, it was shining. Again he showed the twins how to put it together and how to take it apart. When it was packed into the case, Joe handed over the thirty dollars.

"I put the chamois for cleaning it in with the trombone," said the shopkeeper. He followed the boys to the front door. When he saw their bicycles he said, "Can you ride a bike and carry a trombone too?"

"Oh, sure!" said Joe. "I can fasten it onto the handle bars, and I'll ride slowly."

"Well, take care," said the man.

When the boys reached home, they showed the trombone to their mother. "It looks all right," she said. "Now what can you do with it?"

"Why, blow it," said Joe. "Let me show you."

Joe lifted the trombone into position and blew. He blew until he was red in the face, but no sound came out. Then Frank took it. He blew and he blew and he blew, but not a sound did he make.

"Here, let me try it," said Eddie. "You're both weak." Reluctantly Frank handed the trombone to Eddie.

"Here!" said their mother. "If it's going to be handed around like a peace pipe, wipe the mouthpiece off with a paper towel."

Eddie wiped it off, lifted it up, and blew. He too blew until he was red in the face, but he couldn't make a sound.

"See! Didn't I tell you you were too little?" said Frank.

"I did as well as you," said Eddie.

"I can see that you'll need lessons," said Mother. "There must be a trick to it."

"No, there isn't," said Frank. "The man in the store did it easy."

"I guess it will come with a little practice," said Mother.

"We'll get it working soon," said Joe, lifting the lid from the cookie jar.

The boys stood munching cookies. Taking a large bite, Frank said, "Joe, did you see that old hand organ this morning in one of those stores?"

"Wasn't that a wreck?" said Joe.

"I wouldn't give a dollar for it," said Frank.

"Neither would I," said Joe.

Eddie said nothing. He seemed to be thinking deeply while he ate one cookie after another. Soon he was gone. When he returned, he had the hand organ in his arms. The broken strap was trailing. In one hand he had the leg and in the other the handle.

"Eddie!" cried Joe. "How much did you pay for that piece of junk?"

"A dollar," Eddie replied.

"Where's the monkey that goes with it?" asked Frank.

"What do you expect for a dollar?" Eddie asked.

"I'll bet the monkey that went with that organ was walking around when George Washington chopped down the cherry tree," said their father, who had just come home.

"It's a piece of junk," said Joe.

"Well," said Eddie, "when I tried to blow that trombone of yours, I figured maybe the man was right about the organ. When I get my musical instrument together, I won't have to bust myself playing it."

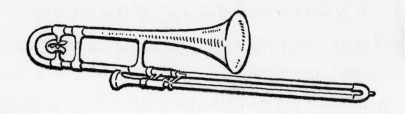

CHAPTER III

A QUIET SUNDAY MORNING

THE twins spent the evening trying to blow the trombone, while Eddie mended his hand organ. By the time they were ready to go to bed, Eddie's organ was in working order and *A Bicycle Built for Two* jangled through the house. The twins, however, had not been able to produce a sound with their thirty-dollar trombone.

Before the boys went upstairs, Mr. Wilson said, "Now tomorrow is Sunday. Let's have a quiet morning. I don't want to hear any drums beaten, horns blown, or organs cranked. I do not want the Wilson brothers to be the neighborhood pests. Is that clearly understood?"

"Yes, sir," said the Wilson brothers in a chorus. They trooped up the stairs.

The following morning the twins were up early. "It's funny we can't make that trombone blow!" said Joe.

"Maybe we can this morning," said Frank. "I was tired last night, but I have a lot of wind this morning. Bet I can make it come right out."

"Dad said we weren't to blow it," said Joe.

"Oh, he didn't mean that we couldn't give one toot," said Frank.

"Well, maybe if it was just a little toot it would be okay," said Joe.

Frank was sitting on the edge of his bed. He lifted the trombone and blew. He blew and he blew and he blew. Not a sound came out.

"Here, let me try," said Joe, who was sitting in the middle of his bed. Joe tried to blow the trombone but the results were the same. "Maybe it's broken," he said.

"Maybe we didn't put it together right," said Frank.

"There isn't any other way to put it together," said Joe.

Meanwhile, Mr. Wilson had gotten up early. He had decided to get rid of a hornets' nest that he had discovered in a gutter under the edge of the side-porch roof. As he walked out to the garage to get a ladder, he met Sidney Stewart. She was carrying her cello under one arm, a music stand under the other, and from her fingers dangled a sheet of music. "Hello, Mr. Wilson!" she said.

"Hello, Sidney!" said Mr. Wilson. "You're out early with your cello."

"Yes," replied Sidney, "I had to get up early to practice. We're having our quartet recital Tuesday night."

"So you are!" said Mr. Wilson. "At the P.T.A. meeting."

"That's right," replied Sidney. "I hope I don't make the mistakes I think I might make."

"I hope not, Sidney," said Mr. Wilson.

Sidney walked on toward the Wilsons' back door. Mr. Wilson wondered why she was taking her cello to their back door. Sidney knocked and Mrs. Wilson opened the door. She, too, was surprised to see Sidney standing there with her cello. "Why, hello, Sidney!" said Mrs. Wilson.

"Hello, Mrs. Wilson," said Sidney. "My Aunt Polly is visiting us and she has her little baby with her, and I have to practice my cello because our quartet concert is Tuesday night. I don't want to wake the baby, so would you please let me practice my cello over here? I can do it in the basement."

"Yes, you can practice in the basement, Sidney," said Mrs. Wilson. "Go on down." Mrs. Wilson opened the cellar door.

"I guess I better take one thing at a time," said Sidney, resting her music stand against the kitchen sink and laying her sheet of music upon the drainboard.

"I think that would be best," said Mrs. Wilson. "There's a stool down there that you can sit on."

"Thank you," said Sidney, as she started down the cellar stairs. She got the cello down safely and came back for the music stand and the sheet of music. "Are you coming Tuesday night to hear the quartet, Mrs. Wilson?" Sidney asked.

"Oh, my, yes!" replied Mrs. Wilson.

"I certainly hope I don't make the mistakes I think I might make," said Sidney.

"Oh, I'm sure you won't," said Mrs. Wilson, as she closed the door behind Sidney. Soon sounds of the cello could be heard in the basement.

Eddie had awakened by this time and his fingers were itching to turn the crank of his organ, but he remembered what his father had said the night before. He got out of bed and picked up the organ. He felt the leg to see if it was on tight. He felt the handle to see if it would turn. He was pleased that everything seemed to be in good working order. All he needed now were a couple of old belts for straps. He wanted so much to turn the handle and play the organ, but he knew that you couldn't play this organ softly. You just played it, and the way it came out was the way it came out—loud!

Suddenly Eddie had an idea. First he spread the down quilt over the bed. Then he carried the organ to his bed and climbed into bed with it. He poked it way down under the covers and crawled in after it. Under the sheets and the blankets and the down quilt, Eddie made a kind of tent. He was delighted with the result. This is like an Eskimo igloo! he said to himself. Then he began to grind his organ and the muffled tune of *A Bicycle Built for Two* tinkled out from the bed.

In the room across the hall, the twins were still trying to blow the trombone. No sound would come out. "I can't understand what's the matter with it," said Frank. Then, for the first time, he turned the instru-

ment around and looked into the trumpet end. "Sure
is dark inside!" he said. Then he poked his hand inside
the horn. His eyes grew big. "Say!" he said. "There's
something in here!"

"What is it?" cried Joe.

"Something," said Frank. Very slowly he withdrew his fingers and there, hanging from them, was a piece of chamois. "It's the chamois," he cried, "the chamois the man in the store used to shine it up with!"

"I remember," said Joe. "He said he was giving us the chamois. Give it a blow now, Frank. Easy though! Just a little blow."

Frank raised the trombone into position and blew.

A small sound came out, a sound like a little grunt.

"That's great!" cried Joe. "Here, let me have a try!" Frank handed the trombone to Joe. Joe wiped the mouthpiece with the sheet and blew, very gently. He produced another small sound.

The boys were delighted. "It plays!" cried Frank. "Let's wake up Eddie. I wish we could give it one good blow."

The twins padded over to Eddie's room in their bare feet. Joe had the trombone. Frank opened the door. "Hi, Eddie!" he called. "Listen to Joe play the trombone." There was no answer. The boys looked at the mound in the middle of Eddie's bed. They could now hear the muffled sound of *The Band Played On.*

"Hey, Eddie!" Joe called.

The music stopped and the mound in the bed began to move. In a moment Eddie stuck his head out from under the covers. Perspiration was running down his face, which was bright red. "What do you want?" he said.

"Listen to me play the trombone," said Joe, placing it to his lips. Once again a small tone came forth.

"I can do it too," said Frank. "Do you want to hear me?"

"No!" replied Eddie, and he crawled back under the covers.

As his brothers closed the door, *A Bicycle Built for Two* rumbled through the bed covers. Joe and Frank went back to their own room.

"Maybe if we aim the trombone out of the window we could give it a real good blow," said Frank. "Dad wouldn't hear it if we aimed it out of our window."

"Let's try it," said Joe.

By this time Mr. Wilson had put up the ladder to the porch roof. He had gathered together the tools for getting rid of the hornets—an insect spray gun and an old broom handle. He stood at the foot of the ladder and looked up at the hornets' nest. "Mary," he called to Mrs. Wilson, who had come to watch. "Will you hold this ladder for me, please?"

Mrs. Wilson came and held the lower part of the ladder as Mr. Wilson started to climb up. "Now be very quiet," he said. "I'll shoot them with this spray gun and douse any hornets that may be up there. Then you hand me that old broom handle and I'll knock the nest down."

Mr. Wilson was near the porch roof now and very close to the window of the twins' room. "Quiet now," he said again to Mrs. Wilson. "We mustn't get them excited." He lifted the spray gun slowly.

At that very moment Joe handed the trombone to Frank and said, "You try it, Frank. Give it all the breath you've got!"

Frank walked to the window and lifted the trombone. He gave it all the breath he had.

Right into his father's ear and right into the hornets' nest came a most terrific blast of sound. It almost knocked Mr. Wilson off the ladder. For one moment the hornets were stunned. Then they came pouring out of the nest in an angry stream.

"Run!" shouted Mr. Wilson to his wife, as he slid down the ladder. "Run for your life!"

Just as they raced frantically around the house with the hornets in hot pursuit, Joe and Frank came out of the back door.

"Dad! Dad!" shouted Joe. "Dad, we can play the trombone!"

"Ouch! He got me!" yelled Mr. Wilson, clapping one hand over his ear.

Both boys stared, open-mouthed, as their father and mother dashed past them and into the kitchen. "Who blew that trombone?" yelled Mr. Wilson.

"I did," said Joe.

"You get upstairs and don't let me hear another sound out of you!" his father shouted.

Eddie came into the kitchen in time to hear his father's order to Joe. Right behind Eddie was Rudy. "Hey, everybody!" he cried. "Look! Bill just brought me these cymbals. Listen!" Rudy clapped them together, and the racket rang through the kitchen with a tremendous clatter. The noise rattled all of the pots and pans.

"Hey, cut it out," said Eddie. "Don't you remember Dad wanted a quiet morning?"

All this time Sidney had been sawing away at her cello down in the basement. Now Mrs. Wilson called to her. "Come along up," she said. "Breakfast is ready, Sidney. Come up and have popovers with us."

"Doesn't anybody want to hear me play the trombone?" said Frank.

"No, Frank!" said his father. "Frankly, no! I don't want to hear anything. I just want to eat my popovers in peace."

"Say, Eddie," said Rudy, "where's Joe?"

"Forget it," said Eddie. "I want to eat my popovers in peace, too."

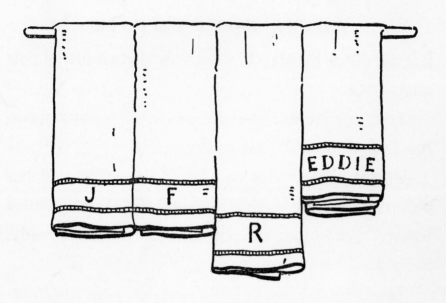

CHAPTER IV

MUSIC IN THE AIR

As the days passed and Eddie listened to the twins practicing on the trombone and Rudy trying to get rhythm into his work on the drums, he began to feel that playing instruments was much harder than he had thought. He didn't think his brothers would be ready to play in an orchestra for years and years. Eddie took a try at his brothers' trombone from time to time. He could make a noise, but it wasn't music; and none of the sounds made by his brothers sounded like music either. He began to wonder whether he would ever find something that he could play in the school orchestra.

At last the day came when the orchestra played for the first time in the school assembly. It was a small group, but Mr. Saunders said it would be getting larger, because there were a lot of boys and girls working hard at their instruments. He added that there were several who would soon be ready for the orchestra. Mr. Saunders also said that he hoped to find some children in the school with very good voices, who could sing with the orchestra.

The children played very well. First they played *The Star-Spangled Banner,* and the whole school stood up and sang. Then they played a march and, finally, a piece that all of the children knew. They sang it through. It was *There's Music in the Air.*

After assembly, each class returned to its own room. Eddie said to Anna Patricia, "Annie Pat, did you get your harp yet?"

"No," said Anna Patricia. "My mother says they're too big. My father says he'd rather get me a baby elephant."

"I'd rather *have* a baby elephant," said Eddie.

When the children who played in the orchestra came into the room, they looked very pleased with themselves. "Boys and girls," said Miss Rice to the small group, "you played beautifully for your first assembly."

The children looked more pleased than ever. Sidney spoke up. "Mr. Saunders says that we're the youngest of all the school orchestras in town. He says maybe we're going to play on TV."

This was too much for Eddie. If the orchestra was going to play on television, he would have to get into that orchestra. He would have to learn to play something besides the hand organ.

The following morning, when Eddie was taking his bath, he suddenly began to sing *There's Music in the Air*. At first he didn't listen to himself. He just sang. But when he got into the second verse, he began to think how good it sounded. He sang louder and louder. His voice hit the tiled walls and rolled around the bathroom. This is great! thought Eddie. I can sing good!

Suddenly he remembered that Mr. Saunders had said that he wanted singers for the orchestra. That's it! thought Eddie. I'm going to sing with the orchestra. He burst into *She'll Be Comin' Round the Mountain*. He sang it over and over again while he slid back and forth in the bathtub.

Finally, through the noise, he heard a pounding on the door. Then he heard Rudy's voice. "Hey, Eddie! What's the big idea? Come out of there! We'll all be late for school."

"Okay!" Eddie called back.

Then he heard his mother's voice. "Edward! Come out of there at once."

"I'm not dry," Eddie called back.

"I don't care if you're not dry," said his mother. "Come out! Rudy and the twins have to get in. Come out at once."

Eddie stepped out of the tub. He threw a towel around himself and, dripping water, he opened the door.

"It's about time!" said Rudy.

"Mama!" Eddie cried. "What do you think? I'm going to be a singer with the orchestra. Did you hear me, Mama?"

"Did I hear you!" exclaimed his mother. "The whole neighborhood heard you."

Eddie ran into his room and began rubbing himself dry. "Wasn't I good, Mama?" he called. "I don't need a musical instrument. I have one inside of me."

His mother had gone downstairs.

Eddie sang *There's Music in the Air* over and over

as he dressed. Then he slid down the banisters, by way of celebrating his great discovery.

He and the twins had to run for the bus. They piled in, and Eddie sat down beside Sidney. The twins sat in the seat opposite. "Hey, Sid," said Eddie, "I can sing."

"So can I," said Sidney.

"Not like me," said Eddie. "Listen to me." He burst forth with his favorite tune, for about the twentieth time that morning.

When he finished, Sidney said, "Well, is that wonderful?"

"You should hear me in the bathtub," said Eddie. "I'm going to be a singer with the orchestra."

"If you can't sing without a bathtub, how can you sing in the orchestra?" said Sidney.

Joe called from across the aisle, "Oh, he'll take the bathtub with him."

"Sure!" said Frank. "Leave it to Eddie!" Then he lifted his voice and called out, "Ladies and gentlemen!

The next number on the program will be Eddie Wilson singing in his bathtub."

All of the children in the bus laughed. "How are you going to get it to school, Eddie?" said Joe.

"Poor Mama!" said Frank. "She'll have to take the bathtub to school every time Eddie sings with the orchestra."

The children roared with laughter. "Go ahead and kid all you want to," said Eddie. "I'll bet I'll be singing with the orchestra before you two can play your trombone."

Now Eddie was determined to sing with the orchestra. He spent all of his allowance on song records. After school he played them over and over until he had memorized each song. As soon as he had memorized a song, he would run up to the bathroom, lock the door, and sing at the top of his voice.

Every morning he had to be dragged out of the bathroom, dripping wet, so that his brothers could get in. As the days went by, Eddie's singing grew louder and louder. Finally, one morning his father said to his mother, "Can't we do something to stop this early-morning racket in the boys' bathroom?"

"Eddie is determined to sing with the orchestra," said Mrs. Wilson.

"Well, he sings with his stomach now," said his father. "I think we'd better send him to a teacher before he bursts wide open."

Mrs. Wilson spent the rest of the week hunting around for a singing teacher for Eddie. On Saturday morning he went for his first lesson and met the teacher his mother had selected. His name was Mr. Duccio.

Mr. Duccio led Eddie to the piano. Mr. Duccio sat down. "Now, Eddie," he said, "I will play for you, and you will sing. What shall it be?"

"She'll Be Comin' Round the Mountain," said Eddie. Eddie loved this song. He could really bring down the roof with *She'll Be Comin' Round the Mountain.*

Mr. Duccio lifted a book down from the top of the piano and said, "I think I have it right here." He leafed

through the pages and found the place. "I shall play it through once," he said. He played it through and then nodded his head for Eddie to begin.

Eddie opened his mouth and put everything he had into the song. When he reached "We'll be singin' hallelujah when she comes," he was red in the face.

When he had finished, Mr. Duccio sat for a moment with his hands resting on the piano keys. Then he said, "Terrible, terrible!"

"You mean my singing?" said Eddie.

"Yes!" replied Mr. Duccio. "Now we shall do it again, and you must sing it very, very softly."

Eddie began again, and Mr. Duccio kept saying, "Softly, softly, softly." When Eddie finished, the teacher said, "It is quite nice when you don't yell."

"Oh, you should hear me in the bathtub, Mr. Duccio," said Eddie. "It sounds better in the bathtub."

"Now," said Mr. Duccio, "we shall have a lesson." He struck one note and held it. "Now sing with me," he said. And he began, "Me, me, me, me, me, me!"

Eddie didn't know what to make of this. It didn't sound like singing to him. "You mean you want me to say me, me, me, me, me, me?"

"That is right," replied Mr. Duccio. "I want you to sing it as I strike each note."

Mr. Duccio went through the scale and Eddie sang, "Me, me, me, me, me, me," on each note.

Mr. Duccio kept saying, "Softly, softly."

When Eddie returned home, his mother said, "Well, Eddie, how did your singing lesson go?"

"Okay," said Eddie. "It sure is a funny kind of a song I learned. Do you want to hear me sing it?"

"Yes, indeed," replied his mother.

"Mr. Duccio says I have to sing it with the piano," said Eddie. "You hit the notes, Mama, and I'll sing."

"What notes?" said his mother.

"Oh, any note," said Eddie. "I can sing this with any notes."

Mrs. Wilson struck one of the keys, and Eddie sang, "Me, me, me, me, me, me."

"Hit another one," said Eddie.

His mother struck another note. "Me, me, me, me, me, me," sang Eddie.

"Beautiful!" said Rudy, as he and the twins came into the room. "Just beautiful!"

"How do you remember those words, Eddie?" said Frank.

"I can sing a song like that, too," said Joe. "Here, puss, puss, puss, puss!"

"Well, it sounds better than your trombone," said Eddie. "And I'm going to sing with the orchestra before you two get into it."

"Oh, yeah?" said the twins in a chorus.

At dinner Eddie said, "I think I'll change my name."

"And what is the matter with your name?" his father asked.

"Oh, it ought to be different," said Eddie. "Now that I'm going to sing with the orchestra and be on TV and everything, I ought to have a real snappy name. I think I'll call myself Bang Wilson."

"I know a better one than that," said Joe.

"What is it?" said Eddie.

"Eddie Hopeless!" replied Joe. Everyone laughed.

"I can just see that in electric lights," said Rudy. "Eddie Hopeless with the Rat-Tail Orchestra."

Eddie grinned. "You just wait and see," he said.

The next morning Joe and Frank and Rudy were all pounding on the bathroom door. Inside, Eddie was sliding back and forth in the tub singing, "Me, me, me, me, me, me."

"You, you, you, you, you come out of there!" yelled Rudy.

CHAPTER V

CALL ME SPIKE

ONE morning Eddie was the center of a group of admiring friends, for he had brought his hand organ to school. There were Boodles and Dumpty, Richard and Davy, all gathered in a bunch. Eddie was grinding out *The Band Played On* when Anna Patricia arrived with a boy about seven years old.

"Hi, Annie Pat!" Eddie called out. "Do you want to see my organ?"

"You showed it to me the other day," said Anna Patricia. Then, nodding her head toward the boy beside her, she said, "This is my cousin. He just moved here from Washington. He's going to be in the second grade. His name is Lionel Cuthbert Lightcap."

No one paid any attention to Lionel Cuthbert Lightcap. Instead they said, "Play some more, Eddie."

Eddie played *A Bicycle Built for Two.*

Lionel Cuthbert Lightcap stared at Eddie through round spectacles with brown rims and tugged gently on a string that was hanging out of his mouth.

"What's on the end of that string?" said Eddie.

"You mean the end in his mouth?" asked Anna Patricia.

"Of course," said Eddie.

"His tooth," replied Anna Patricia. "Anybody could

tell that. He's trying to pull it out." She nudged Lionel Cuthbert and said, "Show them your tooth."

Lionel Cuthbert opened his mouth and displayed his loose tooth. Eddie and his friends crowded around. They could see the string fastened to the tooth. They watched while Lionel Cuthbert gently tugged on the string. The tooth rocked back and forth.

"He isn't working very hard," said Boodles.

"Bet I could pull it out real quick," said Eddie.

"Don't you dare," said Anna Patricia. "He wants to pull it out himself. Don't you, L.C.?"

"Uh-huh!" said Lionel Cuthbert.

"What did you say his name is?" Eddie asked.

"Lionel Cuthbert Lightcap," said Anna Patricia. "We call him L.C."

"You call him what?" said Eddie.

"L.C.," said Anna Patricia.

"Why do you call him Elsie?" said Dumpty. "He's a boy, isn't he?"

"Of course he's a boy!" replied Anna Patricia. "L.

and C. are his initials. He was named after his two grandfathers, Lionel and Cuthbert, but they couldn't decide which to call him, so they call him L.C."

"Elsie!" all the children shouted. "Elsie!"

Lionel Cuthbert took off his spectacles and handed them to Anna Patricia. Anna Patricia noticed that his ears were turning red. This was a bad sign with Lionel Cuthbert. Anna Patricia had seen them turn red before and she knew what would come next. "Don't make him mad!" she cried. "L.C. has a terrible temper."

The warning came too late. As quick as a flash, Lionel Cuthbert rushed upon the group of laughing boys and kicked each one in the shins. Then he ran like a rabbit to the door of the school.

Anna Patricia was left holding his spectacles. "See!" she said to the boys, who were busy rubbing their shins. "I told you not to make L.C. mad." She walked off. Right inside the school door she caught up with her cousin and handed him his spectacles. "L.C., you were very naughty to kick," she said.

"Uh-huh!" said L.C. His string had disappeared. It was all in his mouth.

Anna Patricia led her cousin into the principal's office. Mr. Harris, the principal, looked up and said, "Good morning, Anna Patricia. Who is this?"

"This is my cousin," said Anna Patricia. "He has just moved here from Washington. His mother said that she'd stop in to see you this morning. She sent L.C. with me, so that he could get started in the second grade."

"I see," said Mr. Harris. "What did you say his name is?"

"Lionel Cuthbert Lightcap," said Anna Patricia.

Mr. Harris took out a card and wrote *Lionel Cuthbert Lightcap*.

Anna Patricia opened her mouth again and said, "We call him—"

But Lionel Cuthbert interrupted. "Spike!" he said. "Just Spike."

"Oh!" cried Anna Patricia. Then she saw his ears

turning red. She saw him take off his spectacles. Very quickly she said, "Yes, Mr. Harris. Just Spike."

Spike put his spectacles on. He blinked his eyes and pulled the string out of his mouth.

Mr. Harris looked surprised and said, "What are you doing with that string?"

"He has a loose tooth," said Anna Patricia. "He's trying to pull it out."

"The school nurse could get it out very quickly," said Mr. Harris.

Lionel Cuthbert's ears began to turn red. "Oh, no!" Anna Patricia cried. "He wants to do it himself."

Lionel Cuthbert tugged gently on the string and nodded his head.

"Come with me," said Mr. Harris. "I'll try you in our second grade." Spike followed Mr. Harris to the second-grade room. When they entered the room, the string had disappeared again.

Miss Logan, the teacher, was writing words on the blackboard. She looked up when the door opened.

CALL ME SPIKE

"Good morning, Miss Logan," said Mr. Harris. "I have a new boy for your class. He's Anna Patricia Wallace's cousin. He just moved here from Washington."

"I'm very glad to see you," said Miss Logan, putting out her hand.

"This is Miss Logan, Spike," said Mr. Harris.

"Morning," said Spike, chewing on his string. He shook hands with his teacher.

"I don't suppose your name is really Spike," said Miss Logan.

"It is Lionel Cuthbert Lightcap," said Mr. Harris.

Lionel Cuthbert Lightcap looked up at Miss Logan and said, "They call me Spike."

Miss Logan looked down and thought how much he looked like a little owl. "All right," she said. "We'll call you Spike."

When Mr. Harris left, Miss Logan said, "Now, Spike, put your gum in the wastepaper basket. We don't chew gum in school."

"Not gum," said Spike. He opened his mouth and the little wad of string fell out. When it reached its full length, it hung from his tooth. "Got a loose tooth," he said. "I'm pulling it out." He pulled the string gently.

"Couldn't you give it a good hard pull?" said Miss Logan. "Then it would be out before the children come in."

"I am," said Spike. "It won't come."

Now the bell rang for school to begin, and the children marched into the room. They all looked at Spike, who was standing beside Miss Logan's desk. When they were in their seats, Miss Logan said, "Boys and girls, we have a new friend who has come to be in our second grade. This is—"

"Spike!" said Lionel Cuthbert Lightcap.

"Yes—Spike," said their teacher.

"What's he doing with that string?" said Frances.

"He's trying to pull his tooth out, isn't he?" said George.

Miss Logan gave Spike a seat in the back of the room. The bell rang for school to begin. "Now, Spike," said Miss Logan, "either pull your tooth out, or take the string off. You can't spend the morning pulling that string."

The next time Miss Logan looked at Spike, the string had disappeared. When he went out to recess he was tugging at the string again. There in the schoolyard was Eddie Wilson, entertaining a group of boys and girls with *The Band Played On* and *A Bicycle Built for Two*. Anna Patricia and some other girls were dancing to the music. Spike pushed his way through the ring of children until he was right beside the organ. He was still gently pulling the string on his tooth.

When Eddie saw Spike, he said, "Hello, L—!" But that was as far as he got. L.C. kicked Eddie in the shins for the second time that day. He didn't even take off his spectacles before he kicked.

Eddie almost dropped his hand organ.

Spike turned to run away, but the string on his tooth

caught in the handle of the organ. Like a flash, his tooth was out. When Spike realized what had happened, he began to scream. He ran away from the crowd of children.

Anna Patricia had stopped dancing. She ran to her little cousin. "L.C.!" she said. "I mean Spike! What's the matter?"

"He pulled my tooth out," cried Spike. "I wanted to pull it out myself."

Anna Patricia wiped a little bit of blood off Spike's lip with her handkerchief. "I'm ashamed of you," she said. "Why don't you be brave?"

"'Cause I don't want to be brave," said Spike. "I could be brave if I wanted to be brave. I don't want to be brave. I want my tooth." He cried louder.

Anna Patricia ran to Eddie. "Eddie!" she said. "Where's my cousin's tooth?"

"How do I know where his tooth is?" said Eddie.

"Maybe it went inside the organ," said Anna Patricia.

"If that shin-kicking cousin of yours has gummed up my organ, he'd better keep out of my way," said Eddie. He took hold of the handle to crank it. "Now I have to take the handle off."

Eddie sat down on a step, and a crowd gathered. Joe and Frank appeared. "What's the matter with your organ, Eddie?" said Joe.

"Oh, Anna Patricia's cousin had to go and get his tooth tangled up in my organ," said Eddie.

"His tooth!" exclaimed Frank.

"What did he try to do?" said Joe. "Take a bite out of it?"

"Oh, go blow your trombone!" said Eddie. He had gotten hold of the string now and was unwinding it from around the handle. There was a chorus of, "There it is! There it is!"

At last Eddie held up the string. From the end dangled a tiny tooth. "Here," he said, holding it out to Anna Patricia. "Give him his tooth."

The bell rang for the children to return to their classrooms. Anna Patricia went off to give Spike his tooth, and Joe and Frank went in the opposite direction.

"Doesn't Eddie do the crazy things?" said Frank.

"Sure is a new way to get your teeth pulled," said Joe. "With a hand organ!"

Frank laughed. "Now I bet Eddie thinks he's a dentist," he said.

CHAPTER VI

HEAVENLY HASH

THE school was going to have a fair in order to raise money to buy some instruments for the orchestra. As the day drew near, the children talked about the things that they were going to bring to the fair. Everyone was going to bring something that could be sold.

Anna Patricia said that she was going to bring a wonderful new kind of candy to be sold at the candy table. Sidney said that she was going to bring cakes. Eddie and the twins were gathering together all the books and toys they no longer wanted. These would be sold at the secondhand-book-and-toy table.

One day at recess Anna Patricia said to Sidney, "Wait till you see the wonderful candy I'm going to make for the fair!"

"What kind of candy?" asked Sidney.

"It's called 'heavenly hash,' " said Anna Patricia.

"Hash!" exclaimed Sidney. "I thought hash had meat in it."

"This candy is called 'heavenly hash,' " said Anna Patricia. "You make it out of chocolate, that nice dark kind, and marshmallows and nuts."

"Sounds wonderful!" said Sidney. "I'm going to bring cakes. My mother is going to let me help her make them."

"Oh, I'm going to make the candy all by myself," said Anna Patricia.

The day before the fair, Anna Patricia hurried home

from school to make her candy. "Mother!" she called out as soon as she was inside the front door. "I'm home. Did you get everything I'll need to make the candy?"

"Yes," replied her mother from upstairs. "The chocolate and marshmallows are on the kitchen table, and I put water in the bottom of the double boiler. Just be careful the water doesn't boil away while you melt the chocolate. I greased a dish for you, too."

"Oh, thanks, Mother!" said Anna Patricia. "Where are the nuts?"

"Oh, the nuts are in a little bag in the pantry closet," her mother called back.

"Okay," said Anna Patricia, as she put on her kitchen smock.

"Are you sure you can do it?" her mother called.

"Oh, yes! I can do it," replied Anna Patricia. "I like to do it."

Anna Patricia had just put the chocolate in the top of the double boiler when her cousin Spike arrived. "Hello!" he said. "What are you doing?"

"I'm making heavenly hash," said Anna Patricia.

"What's that?" asked Spike.

"Oh, it's the best candy ever!" said Anna Patricia.

"How soon can we eat it?" said Spike.

"This is for the fair at school," Anna Patricia answered. "It's going to be sold at the candy table."

"Oh!" said Spike. "Can I have some of those little marshmallows?"

"No, you can't," said Anna Patricia. "They're for the heavenly hash."

"Can I help you make it?" asked Spike.

"There isn't anything you can do," replied Anna Patricia.

"Well, can I watch?" said Spike. "I like the smell."

"Yes, if you want to," said Anna Patricia.

The hard chocolate began to melt. Anna Patricia kept the heat low, so that the water in the bottom of the double boiler wouldn't boil away. She remembered that once when she was making heavenly hash, the water did boil away, and the chocolate burned and the candy

110

was spoiled. Anna Patricia didn't want anything to go wrong this time.

She was so interested in watching the lump of chocolate get smaller and smaller that she hardly noticed her father come in the back door. "Hi, Spike!" he said, as he opened the closet door in the pantry and placed something on a shelf.

"Hi, Uncle Charlie!" replied Spike, without taking his eyes off the marshmallows.

"Hello, Anna Patricia!" said her father. "What are you making?"

"I'm making candy for the school fair," replied Anna Patricia.

"And what are you doing, Spike?" said his uncle.

"Just smelling," said Spike.

"Good! Go ahead and smell," said his uncle. "We give smells away around here—free."

Anna Patricia's father went upstairs and said to her mother, "I bought a little bag of seeds for the birds—sunflower seeds. The cardinals like them."

"Oh, I'm glad you thought of it," said Anna Patricia's mother. "I don't know why we've never thought of buying seed for the birds. Maybe we should get a bird feeder."

When the chocolate was all melted, Anna Patricia carried the pan to the table. She poured a thin layer into the bottom of the buttered dish. Then she began laying the little marshmallows on top of the chocolate. When she had them in neat rows, she said, "Oh, Spike! Will you please get the little bag of nuts off the shelf in that closet?" She pointed to the pantry closet with a spoon.

Spike walked to the closet and opened the door. "Do you see them?" asked Anna Patricia.

"Yes," replied Spike. "They are easy to see, 'cause they're in a bag that you can see through."

Spike set the bag down beside Anna Patricia. She opened it and sprinkled half the contents of the bag over the marshmallows. Then she poured more chocolate into the dish, until everything was covered with

chocolate. She began placing a second layer of marshmallows on the soft chocolate.

"Couldn't I have just one of those marshmallows?"
said Spike. "I love marshmallows."

"Yes. Just one," said Anna Patricia.

Spike picked up a marshmallow and ate it. "Can I
have a nut?" he said.

"Yes, you can have a nut—just one," replied Anna
Patricia.

Spike reached into the bag and popped one into his
mouth. He chewed it up. Then he said, "I like the
marshmallows best. Can I have another marshmallow?"

"Just one more," she replied, as she emptied what
was left in the little bag over the second layer of marshmallows. Then she poured all the rest of the chocolate
into the dish and spread it with the spoon. "Doesn't
that look yummy?" she said.

"You bet!" said Spike. "Wish I could have a piece."

"Well, you can't have any, because this is for the

fair," replied Anna Patricia. "You can open the refrigerator door for me, please."

Spike opened the refrigerator door, and Anna Patricia set the dish inside. "Now it will get nice and hard in there," she said, as she closed the door.

That evening Anna Patricia took the candy out of the refrigerator and cut it into square pieces with a sharp knife. She had a large, clean candy box that she had been saving for some time. While her mother put the dishes away, Anna Patricia packed the candy in the box. When she had finished she said, "Look, Mother! Doesn't that look nice?"

"It certainly does," replied her mother. "It looks good enough to eat."

Anna Patricia laughed. "That's what it's for," she said. "This heavenly hash is the best candy ever."

The next morning Anna Patricia carried her box of candy to school and placed it on the table in the hall that had a sign that said *Candy*. As she walked to her room she looked over the long line of tables in the hall. One was marked *Cake*, another said *Books*, and still another, *Preserves*. Near the door of Anna Patricia's room there was a table marked *Flowers*. This table was filled with vases of flowers and potted plants. She could see that down the hall there were more tables.

At the close of school the hall was filled with people who had come to buy at the fair. Many of the children's mothers were behind the tables. Eddie's mother was selling aprons, while Anna Patricia's mother was busy at the flower table. A lot of the children had money to spend, and they crowded around the candy table.

It took Eddie a long time to decide which box of candy he wanted to buy. He was buying it for his birthday party, and he wanted the very best. The birthday party was going to be at school, for his whole class, so the box had to be large. He looked at every box and finally picked out one that looked especially good. One of the mothers wrapped it up for him.

As Eddie was leaving school, he passed Anna Patricia. "Hi, Annie Pat!" he said. Then he held up his package and said, "You're going to get some of this at my birthday party tomorrow."

That evening Anna Patricia's father looked into the closet for the bag of birdseed he had bought. It was not where he remembered putting it. He moved things around on the shelves, but the only bag he found was a bag of nuts. "Where did all those sunflower seeds go?" he asked his wife.

"I didn't see them," she replied.

"Anna Patricia!" her father called into the living room. "Did you see a little bag of sunflower seeds?"

"I don't know what they look like," replied Anna Patricia.

Her father looked down and saw one on the floor. He picked it up. "Here, I'll show you one," he said, coming into the living room.

Anna Patricia looked at the seed on the palm of her father's hand. "Oh!" she said. "Is that a sunflower seed?"

"Yes, that's a sunflower seed," said her father.

"Why, I thought they were nuts," said Anna Patricia. "I put them in the heavenly hash."

"What is heavenly hash?" her father asked.

"It's that wonderful candy I made to sell at the fair," replied Anna Patricia.

"Heavenly hash!" exclaimed her father. "It must be wonderful! I wonder who bought it."

"Oh, dear!" said Anna Patricia. "I guess they won't like it."

"I'm afraid they won't," said her father.

The following day, just after school was out, Eddie's mother drove up to the school with a big box. She took it into Eddie's room and put it on a chair near the door. "Have a nice party," she said as she left the room.

"Thank you," said Miss Rice. Then she turned to Eddie and said, "Come unpack your refreshments, Eddie." Eddie walked over to the big box and opened it up, while Miss Rice passed out paper plates.

First Eddie lifted out a big box of cupcakes. He handed this box to Boodles. "Pass them around," he said. Then he brought out little paper cups of ice cream. Sidney and Miss Rice helped Eddie distribute these. Finally Eddie opened his box of candy from the fair. He walked down the aisle, holding the box out to each child in the first row.

"M-m-m! Doesn't that look good!" said Margie, when she took a piece.

"Oh! Chocolate and nuts!" said Davy, when Eddie offered it to him.

Eddie started on the second row of children. He held the box out to Anna Patricia. Anna Patricia took a piece and looked at it. Then she cried, "Oh, Eddie! That candy has birdseed in it!"

Everyone in the class laughed.

Eddie laughed and looked around the class. "Did you hear that?" he cried. "She says it has birdseed in it."

"Birdseed!" cried Boodles. "Tweet! Tweet!"

"It does so have birdseed in it," said Anna Patricia.

"Anna Patricia, you're nuts!" said Eddie.

"She's as nutty as the nuts in this candy," said Dumpty.

"They are not nuts," said Anna Patricia. "They are birdseeds."

"Now, Anna Patricia," said Miss Rice, "what makes you think they are birdseeds?"

"Well, you see," said Anna Patricia, "that's the heavenly hash I made for the fair, and my cousin gave me the wrong bag. I put a bag of birdseed into the candy instead of a bag of nuts. That's how I know it's birdseed."

The whole first row rushed to the front of the room to spit out their candy into the wastepaper basket. Rosalie began to cry. "Oh, Miss Rice! I swallowed some of it. What shall I do?"

"It won't hurt you, Rosalie," said Miss Rice.

Eddie put the lid on the box and said, "I guess I'll take it home for the birds."

"Maybe you'd better eat it yourself, Eddie," said Boodles. "Maybe this birdseed hash will make you sing better."

CHAPTER VII

MONKEY BUSINESS

IT WAS October, and Halloween was drawing near. All the children were looking forward to the Halloween parade and the class parties. Of course, everyone was hoping to surprise everyone else, but it was hard for some of the children to keep secrets.

Sidney kept changing her mind about what she would be on Halloween. Every time she made up her mind she had to tell somebody. By the middle of October she had told Eddie that she was going to be a cow girl, a skeleton, a witch, a ghost, a scarecrow, a clown, and a snake charmer.

Eddie had no trouble deciding. He was going to be an organ-grinder. He already had the most important part of the costume, the organ. What he needed was a monkey, and he didn't know where he could get one. He knew he couldn't get a live one and he didn't have a toy one. He decided one day to look for a toy one in the ten-cent store.

Eddie rode to the store on his bicycle. He locked his bike outside and went in the store. At the candy counter he bought himself a little bag of candy corn. Then he went to the toy counter. He looked over all the toys, but there was no monkey.

Eddie was just about to walk away, when he looked up at the Halloween masks that were hung on a heavy cord above the counter. As he raised his head, he looked right into the face of a monkey. It was a rubber mask made to fit over one's head. As Eddie looked up at the

126

monkey face, he suddenly had one of his bright ideas. Sidney could be his monkey. A monkey was much better than anything Sidney had told him she wanted to be.

Eddie bought the mask and rode home. He could hardly wait to tell Sidney about his idea. As soon as he reached home, he called to Sidney. "Hi! Sid!" he shouted. Sidney appeared at a side window. She beckoned to Eddie to come in.

Eddie reached Sidney's front door just as she opened it. "Hi, Sid!" he said. "I have a wonderful idea for Halloween."

"I'm practicing my cello," said Sidney, "but come in. What's the idea?"

Eddie threw himself on the sofa, and Sidney sat on the floor beside her music stand. Her cello was resting against a chair.

"You know my hand organ," said Eddie.

"Sure!" said Sidney. "Do you want to trade it for something?"

"Nope," said Eddie. "I want a monkey to go with it."

"Swell!" said Sidney. "Where are you going to get one?"

"Right here!" said Eddie. He pounded on the sofa with his fist. "Right here."

"Are you crazy, Eddie?" said Sidney. "You know that I don't have a monkey."

"Look!" said Eddie, pulling the monkey mask out of his pocket. He put the mask over his head and pulled it down to cover his face.

Sidney jumped up. "Oh, Eddie!" she cried. "Are you going to be a monkey on Halloween, or an organ-grinder? You can't be both, can you?"

"I'm going to be the organ-grinder," replied Eddie. Then he pointed to Sidney and said, "You're going to be the monkey."

Sidney laughed and laughed. "Oh, Eddie!" she gasped. "That's wonderful. Here, let me put it on right away."

Eddie took off the mask and handed it to Sidney. "We'll go into the parade together," said Eddie. "I have it all figured out. I'll grind my organ and have you on the end of a rope."

"And I'll carry a tin cup and tip my hat and dance around," said Sidney, pulling the monkey mask down over her face. "How do I look?" she asked.

Eddie shouted with delight. "That's great!" he cried. "I can't wait for Halloween to come. We'll be the hit of the school parade."

Just then Sidney heard a car door slam. "Oh!" she cried. "Here comes my mother, and I haven't practiced my cello. You better go home, Eddie." Eddie scooted out the back door.

Without thinking of the mask that she was wearing, Sidney picked up her cello. She placed it in front of her and began playing a sweet lullaby, called *Sleep, Little One, Sleep.*

Mrs. Stewart came in the front door with a big bag of groceries. She heard Sidney playing her cello. Sidney was playing very well. It was sweet music. Mrs. Stewart stopped at the living-room door to listen.

Sidney looked up at her mother and smiled sweetly, but her mother could not see Sidney's sweet smile. What she saw was the head of a monkey coming out of a pink collar with white ruffles and with a pink bow under its chin.

Mrs. Stewart dropped the whole bag of groceries. Apples, oranges, cans of soup, boxes of frozen vegetables, and a bag of dried Lima beans went rolling all over the living-room floor. The bag of beans broke and the beans flew everywhere.

This stopped the cello music. "Oh, Mum!" cried Sidney. "What's the matter?"

"Oh, Sidney!" her mother cried. Mrs. Stewart began to laugh. She laughed so hard she had to lean against the wall. Then she sat down on the stairs and rocked back and forth.

Sidney couldn't believe that her mother was laughing about the groceries and beans that were all over the

floor. She wondered whether her mother could be crying. She had never seen her mother cry. "I'll pick them up, Mummie. I'll pick them up!" said Sidney, dropping on her knees.

"Oh, Sidney!" her mother gasped. "You do look so funny. Where did you get that horrible mask?"

Now Sidney remembered that she was still wearing the monkey mask. She pulled it off. "Eddie gave it to me," she said, laughing. "It's Eddie's idea. He's going to be an organ-grinder on Halloween, and I am going to be his monkey."

When all the groceries and all the beans had been collected, Sidney said, "Will you make a costume for me, Mum?"

"Oh, yes! I'll make a monkey costume for you," her mother replied.

"Just like an organ-grinder's monkey?" Sidney asked.

"Yes," her mother said. "I'll make a short plaid kilt and a little red jacket with gold braid."

"And I have to have a little red hat, like a pillbox, with a strap under my chin," said Sidney.

"I can make that out of an old red felt hat that's up in the attic," said her mother.

"And I have to have a tail," said Sidney. "Can you make a tail?"

"I think I can make a tail," replied her mother.

Mrs. Stewart made Sidney a suit of dark-brown woolly material. It covered her from her feet to her neck. It had long sleeves that ended in fingers, like gloves. This was the monkey's skin. Sidney wanted a very long tail. It was made of the same brown material and was stuffed with cotton. "Sew it on very good, Mum," said Sidney, "so that nobody can pull it off."

Mrs. Stewart sewed it on with carpet thread. As she pulled the needle through, she said, "No one will pull this off."

When the kilt and the red jacket were finished, and the red felt hat fitted properly, Sidney could hardly wait for Halloween to come. Eddie was impatient too. His costume was ready. He had a large nose to wear, and long black mustachios. He had brown baggy trousers, a checked shirt, and an old brown felt hat of his father's.

The day before Halloween, Eddie and Sidney rehearsed their act in the Stewarts' living room. All went well. Sidney danced like a monkey on the end of Eddie's rope. She had a little trouble managing her tail. Once Eddie stepped on it, and Sidney cried, "Eddie! Get off my tail!" No sooner had she said this than she stepped on it herself, and almost fell flat.

"Sid!" said Eddie. "I think your tail is too long. You're going to have tail trouble, sure as shootin'."

"Oh, no! It's all right," said Sidney. "It's sewed on with carpet thread."

"Okay!" said Eddie. "We're going to roll 'em in the aisles tomorrow when we parade into the auditorium."

The following day all the children were excited about the Halloween parade and the parties. In the morning it was hard for them to think about their lessons.

Most of the children had brought their costumes with them, but Sidney's mother came for her at noon. She drove her home to put on the monkey costume. They were also bringing cupcakes back with them, and a jack-o'-lantern filled with peanuts, for the party.

When they returned to school, Mrs. Stewart parked the car by the curb in front of the school. "Can you manage these things, Sidney?" she asked. "If you can, I'll leave the car here and go do my marketing."

"Oh, yes!" said Sidney. "I'll take the cupcakes in and come back for the jack-o'-lantern."

"Very well," said her mother. "Just be sure you lock the car door when you finish unloading."

"All right!" said Sidney. "I'll remember."

Sidney's mother went off to do her marketing, and Sidney carried the box of cupcakes into the school. She carried her tail over her arm, like a train on a ball gown.

Inside the school there was a hum of children's voices coming from the open doors of the classrooms. Children in costumes scurried through the halls. On her way to her room, Sidney met a fairy, a bride, a red devil walking arm in arm with an angel, a canary bird sucking a lollipop, Red Ridinghood, and a butterfly having trouble with her garters.

When Sidney appeared in her classroom, all the children called out, "Oh! Look at the monkey! Who's the monkey?"

Sidney whispered to Eddie, "I'll be back in a minute." She went back to the car for the jack-o'-lantern. She forgot to hold her tail, and when she ran down the steps, the tail went bump-bump-bump-bump-bump-bump, all the way down the steps.

Sidney opened the car door and stepped inside the car to get the jack-o'-lantern. It was on the back seat. She picked it up and stepped out of the car. She remembered that her mother had told her to lock the car door, so she pushed down the little lock button on the door. She had the jack-o'-lantern in her left arm. With her right hand she slammed the door shut. Then she turned and started off. She took two steps, but on the third she was pulled back with a jerk. She looked behind her to see what was the matter. She soon found out. It was tail trouble, as Eddie had said. She had locked the door on her tail.

Sidney took hold of the handle of the door, hoping that it had not locked; but it was locked tight, and only the key would open it. The key was in her mother's purse.

Sidney looked around. There wasn't anyone in sight. It was very close to one o'clock, when the parade would start. Everyone was inside the school. She opened her mouth and yelled, "Help! Help! Help!"

No one appeared.

Inside the school the children were marching into the auditorium. Where is Sidney, thought Eddie. He couldn't go in without his monkey. Where had she gone? He went to the front door to see if he could see her. He opened the door. Then he heard someone calling, "Help! Help! Help!"

Eddie rested his hand organ against the steps and ran out to Sidney. "What's the matter?" he cried.

"My tail's caught in the door," said Sidney.

"Well, open the door," said Eddie.

"I can't. It's locked," said Sidney.

"I told you that tail was too long," said Eddie.

"Well, do something!" cried Sidney.

Eddie ran back into his classroom and returned with a pair of scissors. "Here!" he said. "I'll have to cut it off." He knelt down and started to hack off Sidney's tail. It was hard to cut the heavy cotton stuffing.

"Hurry up!" said Sidney.

"It's tough," said Eddie.

At last he cut through the tail, and Sidney was free. The organ-grinder and his monkey ran up the steps and through the door. Eddie picked up his hand organ and hooked a leash onto Sidney's belt. Now they were ready to follow the parade. When they reached the stage of the auditorium, everyone clapped.

Eddie ground out *The Band Played On,* and Sidney danced. She danced just like an organ-grinder's monkey. She tipped her little red hat when Mr. Harris put a penny in her mother's measuring cup.

When Mrs. Stewart came back from her marketing, a black cocker spaniel was lying beside her car chewing on the remains of Sidney's tail. So! said Mrs. Stewart to herself. There must have been tail trouble.

At three o'clock, when all of the parties were over, Eddie's mother came for Eddie and Sidney and, of course, the hand organ. They drove away from the school and stopped for a red light at the corner.

Eddie was looking out of the window while Sidney told Mrs. Wilson all about the parade and the parties. Suddenly Eddie cried out, "Look, Sid! There goes a cocker spaniel with the end of your tail!"

CHAPTER VIII

CHOCOLATE-COVERED MARSHMALLOWS

THE orchestra was growing larger every week. With the money made at the fair, the school had been able to buy a number of instruments and a lot of music. Both of the Wilson twins were now in the orchestra. Joe was playing one of the school's trombones.

Every child in the orchestra was working hard, because Mr. Saunders had announced that they had been invited to play on a television program during Education Week. The child with the best voice in the school was going to sing several songs with the orchestra.

Eddie had thought of asking if he could borrow a trumpet or a flute, but he knew that he would never be able to learn to play either one in time for the TV concert. He decided to stick to his singing and hoped to be the one chosen to sing the songs.

The school had not bought a harp, so Anna Patricia had given up the idea of playing one. She was now practicing on a clarinet and would be in the orchestra soon.

One day Eddie found himself sitting beside Anna Patricia in the lunchroom. "Oh, Eddie!" said Anna Patricia. "It's too bad you can't be in the orchestra. I guess you know that we're going to be on TV."

"Sure! Everybody knows that," said Eddie. "I'm going to sing the songs."

Anna Patricia laughed. "You—the vocalist! You couldn't be the vocalist!" she said.

Eddie hooted. "Annie Pat," he said, "you and Sid sure do use fancy words!"

"Well, *vocalist* is right," said Anna Patricia. "You should try to speak better English. And I know that you're not the vocalist. I know that you have to try out for that. You have to have an addition."

Eddie hooted again. "Addition!" he said. "You mean *audition,* Annie Pat. You should try to speak better English."

"Well anyway, I know all about it," said Anna Patricia. "My cousin Lionel Cuthbert Lightcap is going to addition—I mean audition."

"You mean Cousin Elsie?" said Eddie. "That shin kicker?"

"Just you wait," said Anna Patricia. "Just you wait and see. My cousin has sung on TV already. You've never even been inside a TV studio."

"What difference does that make?" said Eddie.

"It means," said Anna Patricia with her nose in the air, "that you are not as good as my cousin. He gets paid for singing."

This seemed to impress Eddie. Maybe this shin kicker was really good. "How much does he get paid?" he asked.

"He gets a box of chocolate-covered marshmallows every time he sings," said Anna Patricia.

"Chocolate-covered marshmallows!" exclaimed Eddie. "That's not much!"

"Well, it makes him sing," said Anna Patricia.

"Who pays him those chocolate-covered marshmallows?" said Eddie.

"His father," said Anna Patricia. "And my cousin has to see them before he will sing."

"Doesn't he like to sing?" said Eddie.

"Oh, no!" replied Anna Patricia.

"Then why does he?" said Eddie.

"Because he likes chocolate-covered marshmallows," said Anna Patricia.

"You know what?" said Eddie.

"What?" asked Anna Patricia.

"That little shin-kicking cousin of yours is spoiled," said Eddie.

"That's what my mother says," said Anna Patricia. "But he will be the vocalist, because my Aunt Jane says so. You wait and see."

Eddie waited. When the day came for the audition, five children had been selected to try out, from the whole school. Spike and Eddie were among them. They all sat on one side of the auditorium stage, waiting for their turn to sing. The auditorium was empty, all but the front row. There sat Mr. Harris, the principal, and Miss Black, the music teacher; Spike's mother and father were there too. His father was holding something that looked like a box of candy. Bet they're the chocolate-covered marshmallows, thought Eddie.

When Spike's turn came to sing, he walked to the front of the stage and looked down at the box on his father's knee. A smile lit his face. He opened his mouth

and sang *Carry Me Back to Old Virginny*. Anyone would have thought that he was always as good as gold.

Miss Black leaned over and said to Spike's mother, "He looks so happy when he sings. It's wonderful! He looks just like a little angel."

Spike's mother smiled. "He's very musical," she said.

As soon as Spike had finished, his father lifted him down from the stage. Spike sat down beside his father and began unwrapping the box. He lifted the lid, and without asking anyone to have some, he began stuffing chocolate-covered marshmallows into his mouth.

The whole time Eddie was singing *Oh, Susanna!* his mouth was watering for one of those chocolate-covered marshmallows. When it was over, he hoped that he had sung better than anyone else. He wanted so much to be on the television program.

The following day Mr. Saunders asked Eddie to come to his room. Mr. Saunders was alone when Eddie arrived. "Eddie," he said, "I know how much you

151

wanted to be the one chosen to sing with the orchestra on the TV show, and I'm sorry to have to tell you that the little Lightcap boy was chosen. You sing very well, Eddie, but Mr. Harris and Miss Black felt that we should have the little Lightcap fellow. They say they chose him because his face just shines when he sings."

Eddie looked down at the floor. "Well," he said. Then he swallowed hard. "Well, that's okay."

"You've been taking lessons, haven't you, Eddie?" said Mr. Saunders.

"Yes, sir," said Eddie, still looking at the floor.

"Have you learned to read notes?" asked Mr. Saunders.

"Pretty good," replied Eddie.

"You have a fine sense of rhythm," said Mr. Saunders.

"Thanks," replied Eddie, and he blinked his eyes very hard to keep back the tears that he was afraid might show.

"I don't have any instrument now for you," said Mr. Saunders, "but as soon as I do I'll let you have it. Then you can be in the orchestra."

"Thanks," replied Eddie.

Mr. Saunders put his hand on Eddie's shoulder and looked down on the top of his bowed head. "I'm sorry, Eddie," he said, "but I think I'll have something for you soon."

"Thanks," said Eddie.

Eddie walked all the way home. He didn't want to see any of his friends on the bus. He didn't want to run into Anna Patricia and hear her say, "I told you so!"

That little shin kicker! thought Eddie. That marshmallow eater! He doesn't want to sing. He just wants marshmallows! It isn't fair! It was a long, long walk, and Eddie walked slowly. He stopped and looked in the shop windows, but nothing made him feel happy.

As he neared his own neighborhood, he kicked the leaves that had fallen from the trees. Now the air was

filled with the odor of burning leaves. He sniffed it.
Nice smell, he thought. It was the first thought that
had pushed Spike out of Eddie's mind since he had
left school.

Eddie went into the house through the kitchen door.
He knew that was where his mother would be. "Hello,
Eddie!" she said, when he came in. "We're going to
have your favorite dinner tonight. Everything that
you like best."

"What are we going to have, Mama?" said Eddie.

"First, grapefruit with maple syrup," said his
mother. "Lots of maple syrup. Then Aunt Minnie's
giant hamburgers with 'the works.' " "The works," to
Eddie, were ketchup, chili sauce, chowchow, pepper
hash, piccalilli, tomatoes, and onions.

"And I made a strawberry-ice-cream pie for des-
sert," said Mother. "Father won't be home for dinner, so you boys can have your dinner on trays and
watch television." Mrs. Wilson leaned over and kissed
her littlest boy.

"Mama," said Eddie, "I'm not going to be on TV."

"I know, darling," said his mother. "The twins heard about it. They told me."

Eddie leaned against his mother, and she put her arm around him. "Now everything is going to be all right," she said. "Run upstairs and wash your face and hands and comb your hair."

The four boys sat in front of the television and ate their dinner. It was a good western movie. It made Eddie think of the months he had once spent with Aunt Minnie and Uncle Ed on their big ranch in Texas.

It was the twins' night to help with the dishes, so after dinner Eddie went up to his room. On his door he hung one of the many signs that he had collected. It said *Do Not Disturb*. Then he closed the door. He took his old hand organ out of the closet and sat down on his bed.

Soon his mother could hear *The Band Played On* coming from Eddie's room. Suddenly the back door opened, and Mr. Wilson came in. He was carrying a big, flat black box.

"Why, I thought you were going to be late," said Mrs. Wilson in surprise.

"I left the office right after you phoned me," replied Mr. Wilson. "I have something for Eddie. Where is he?"

"He's upstairs in his room," said Mrs. Wilson. "He's playing his hand organ."

"Well, come on up, everybody," said Mr. Wilson.

The twins left their jobs and followed their father and mother and Rudy up the stairs. "What is it, Dad?" said Joe.

"Wait and see," said his father. He knocked on Eddie's door. "Eddie!" he called.

"Come in," Eddie called back.

Mr. Wilson opened the door. "Son," he said, "I brought you something!"

"What is it, Dad?" said Eddie.

Mr. Wilson placed the box on the bed. He opened

156

the fasteners on the side of the box and lifted the lid. Inside lay a musical instrument that Eddie had never seen before. It had metal bars of different lengths and two small hammers. "What is it?" he asked.

"Most people call it a set of bells," said his father. "It has a wonderful German name—glockenspiel."

"Glockenspiel!" Eddie exclaimed.

"I telephoned Mr. Saunders and asked him if he thought you could learn to play it," his father said.

"What did he say?" Eddie interrupted.

"He said it would be duck soup for you. He said you have the rhythm."

"Can I play it in the orchestra?" said Eddie.

"You certainly can," his father replied. "You will be in the orchestra long before that TV performance comes up."

Eddie put his hand out, and his father took it in his. "Thanks, Dad!" he said. "Thanks!" Then he threw his arms around his father's neck. "It's super!" he said. "Super!"

Eddie sat on his bed for a long time, picking out tunes on the bells. When his mother said that he must go to bed, he placed the instrument on a chair, so close to his bed that he could reach out and touch it.

When the light was out, he remembered that his mother had said that everything would be all right. He reached out and touched his bells. Everything *was* all right.

CHAPTER IX

EDDIE AND THE GLOCKENSPIEL

THE following morning Eddie rushed over to Sidney's with his bells. He was disappointed when he found that Sidney and her father and mother had gone away for the week end.

He went home and decided to telephone Anna Patricia. He had to tell somebody about his musical instrument. When Anna Patricia answered the telephone, he said, "Hey, Annie Pat! What do you think?"

"What?" said Anna Patricia.

"I'm going to be in the orchestra," said Eddie.

"You're not going to be the vocalist," said Anna Patricia. "My cousin's going to be it."

"Oh, I'm going to play an instrument," said Eddie.

"What are you going to play?" Anna Patricia asked.

"A glockenspiel," said Eddie.

"A what?" said Anna Patricia.

"A glockenspiel," said Eddie, a little louder.

"I can't understand you," said Anna Patricia. "You should speak better English, Eddie."

"I'm not speaking English," said Eddie. "I'm speaking German."

"German!" exclaimed Anna Patricia. "You don't know any German, Eddie."

"I do so!" said Eddie. "I just learned it."

"Well, what can you say?" said Anna Patricia.

"Glockenspiel!" said Eddie.

"What does it mean?" asked Anna Patricia.

"It's the instrument I'm going to play in the orchestra," said Eddie.

"Well, I never heard of it," said Anna Patricia, "and I don't believe there is such a thing."

"Yes, there is," replied Eddie. "You just listen, and I'll play it for you. I'll let you hear it." Eddie placed the telephone right beside his instrument. He picked up the hammers and struck the bells. He played a little tune. Then he picked up the telephone and said, "Did you hear it?"

"Yes," Anna Patricia replied. "It just sounded like bells."

"That's what it is—glockenspiel!" said Eddie. "You'll see it on Monday. It's super."

Eddie hung up, and Anna Patricia said to her mother, "Now Eddie Wilson is speaking German. Really! And he says he's going to be in the orchestra."

"What is he going to play?" her mother asked.

"He says it's a—a—spielglocken," said Anna Patricia.

"Spielglocken!" said her mother. "I never heard of it."

"It just sounds like bells," said Anna Patricia.

Eddie could hardly wait for Monday morning to come. The week end had never seemed so long before. On Monday he would go to the orchestra rehearsal. When Miss Rice said, "The boys and girls in the orchestra may go to rehearsal," he would get up and go along with Davy Hawkins and Sidney and the others who were in the orchestra. He would be rehearsing with them for the television performance.

On Monday morning Mrs. Stewart drove Sidney with her cello and Eddie with his case of bells to school. Sidney said, "I think your instrument is swell!" She especially liked its German name—glockenspiel.

At school things did not work out just as Eddie had expected. At half past nine Mr. Saunders sent for him.

Eddie carried his case down the hall to Mr. Saunders' office.

When Eddie opened the door, Mr. Saunders saw a very different boy from the one he had said good-by to on Friday afternoon. This was a very happy Eddie indeed.

"Hello, Eddie," said Mr. Saunders. "Let me see your bells." Eddie placed the case on a table, opened the clasps, and lifted the lid.

Mr. Saunders placed a sheet of music on the stand and said, "Now let's see what you can do with this."

Eddie began to play, but he found that playing from notes was not as easy as picking tunes out by ear. He began to look worried.

"It's all right, Eddie," said Mr. Saunders. "You will have to learn how to play it."

"But I played it all right over the week end," said Eddie.

"That wasn't playing, Eddie," said Mr. Saunders. "That was picking."

"Do you think I'll be able to play it in time for the TV concert?" asked Eddie.

"If you work at it, I'm sure you will be," said Mr. Saunders.

Eddie stayed with Mr. Saunders for a half hour, working on his bells. He didn't go to orchestra rehearsal. This was a disappointment, but Mr. Saunders had said it wouldn't be long before he could be part of the orchestra. Eddie worked hard all during the week, and the following Monday, when he went to Mr. Saunders for a lesson, he did quite well.

It was not long before Eddie went to practice with the orchestra. This was a very important day to Eddie. His place was right beside Anna Patricia.

It took some time for the violins to tune up, but at last Mr. Saunders raised his stick. "Eddie," he said, "you know where to come in, don't you?"

"Yes, sir," said Eddie.

"I know where he comes in," said Anna Patricia. "I have been helping him."

EDDIE AND THE GLOCKENSPIEL

"Eddie is the one who has to know where he comes in," said Mr. Saunders. "Now, all ready?"

Everyone was ready, and the orchestra began to play a waltz. Eddie watched his music carefully, and when it was time for him to play the bells, he came in right on the beat. As he struck the bells and the sound blended with the rest of the instruments, he felt a tingling that went up his back and his neck, right up into his hair.

Eddie thought the music was beautiful. He hadn't ever thought that music was so beautiful, and he was doing something that made it beautiful. He wasn't just being in something important. He was making music.

Now it was time for the bells to be silent for a minute. Eddie held his hammers and looked up at the ceiling. He was listening to the music. When it was time for Eddie's bells to come in again, Mr. Saunders nodded to Eddie, but Eddie was busy looking at the ceiling and thinking how beautiful the music was.

Anna Patricia saw Mr. Saunders nod, and she knew

that it was time for Eddie's bells. She took her clarinet out of her mouth and said, "Hey, Spielglocken! Wake up!"

This stopped the music. Everyone, including Mr. Saunders, laughed. Eddie's face turned red.

"Eddie," said Mr. Saunders, "you will have to keep awake."

"Oh, I'm sorry," said Eddie.

That was the morning that Eddie Wilson became Eddie Spielglocken.

Eddie kept his mind on his work after that, and he did very well, but all the boys and girls in the orchestra called him Eddie Spielglocken. His brothers Joe and Frank thought it was a wonderful name. Eddie didn't care what they called him. He was happy. He was in the orchestra at last.

On his way home from school in the car beside Sidney, he said, "Say, Sid, I didn't know making music was like that!"

"Like what?" said Sidney.

"Oh, I don't know," said Eddie. "But making music is pretty neat, isn't it?"

"I told you, Eddie, that it was nice to make music," said Sidney.

"Yeah, I know," he said.

When Eddie reached home, his mother said, "Eddie, please start raking up the leaves. I've never seen so many."

"Okay," said Eddie. "First can I have a peanut-butter sandwich?"

"Certainly," said his mother. "Have a glass of milk with it, and an apple."

Eddie ate his sandwich and drank his milk. Then he went out to rake leaves.

"Leaves, leaves, leaves," said Eddie, thinking aloud. "Always raking leaves." He looked up at the trees. There were still an awful lot up there. He leaned on his rake and ate his apple. He looked up at a big maple tree that was in front of the house. It had turned to gold, and some of the branches were tipped with flaming red. As the sun shone on the tree, it was brilliant. Eddie watched a red leaf fall at his feet. He stooped down and picked it up. He laid it on the palm of his hand and looked at it. Then suddenly he dropped his rake and ran into the house. "Mama!" he called. "Mama, look!" Eddie handed the leaf to his mother and said, "Isn't that beautiful?"

"It certainly is," said his mother.

"Did you see that tree out front, Mama?" said Eddie. "Come look out of the front window." Mrs. Wilson followed Eddie to the front window. "Look," said Eddie. "Isn't that pretty?"

"It is indeed, Eddie," said his mother.

"And I'll bet you never noticed this," said Eddie. "When the sun shines on it, it's brighter. See, it looks like real gold when the sun shines on it."

"Yes, it does," said his mother.

"And look! Look, Mama! Look at the leaves coming down."

Mrs. Wilson stood by the window with her arm

around Eddie. Eddie champed on his apple. He swal-lowed and said, "You know the way those leaves come down—sorta floaty? Well, you know that's the way I feel sometimes."

"When do you, Eddie?" his mother asked.

"Well, when I hear music, and when it's real pretty. I feel just like those leaves—sorta floaty. I don't know exactly, but I like music, Mama. Sid's cello used to sound like an old cow, but it doesn't sound that way any more. And when I played the bells with the or-chestra this morning, it was super!"

"I remember when you only liked to play ball," said his mother.

Eddie laughed and took another big bite of his ap-ple. He crunched it up, gulped, and said, "I guess I'm musical, Mama."

Just then the twins came stamping in the back door. "Hello, Mother," they called out.

"Oh, boy!" cried Joe. "Do we have a lot of leaves to rake!"

"Yes!" said Frank. "Leaves, leaves, nothing but leaves. Do I hate those things!"

"Oh, they make good bonfires," said Joe. "Come on, Eddie Spielglocken. Don't sit down on the job just because Frank and I are here. Back to your rake, Eddie Spielglocken!" The boys laughed, and Eddie went out with them to rake the leaves.

In a moment he was back. He whispered to his mother, "Mama! Don't tell the twins what I said about the leaves."

"Not a word, Eddie," said his mother. "Not a word."

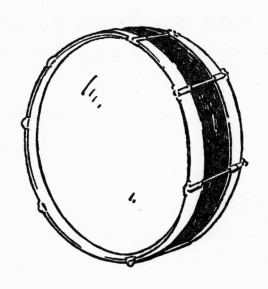

CHAPTER X

THE TELEVISION PROGRAM

THE orchestra had been rehearsing for weeks for the television concert. Mr. Saunders was pleased with the children's work. They practiced at home, and this meant that the rehearsals went well.

Spike Lightcap, as everyone except his mother now

called him, was to sing three songs at the concert, so the orchestra had been practicing *Home on the Range, Blow the Man Down,* and *Auld Lang Syne.* Spike came to each orchestra rehearsal and sang his three songs. It took a great many rehearsals before Mr. Saunders was satisfied with the orchestral accompaniment. By the time he was pleased, every child in the orchestra knew the words of the songs by heart. At home the twins whistled the tunes over and over, and Eddie sang them every time he took a bath.

Mr. Saunders had made his plans very carefully. The children were to go to the television station in school buses. Each child was to take care of his own instrument and be sure to have it with him when he reached the studio. The concert was to go on the air at nine-thirty in the morning, which meant that the buses would have to leave the school promptly at eight-thirty. Mr. Saunders told the children that everyone must be at the school by eight o'clock. This was a half hour earlier than anyone had ever got to school before.

178

The thing that had not been planned was the weather. It had begun to snow the day before the performance. It went right on snowing all night and turned into the first blizzard of the winter.

Mrs. Wilson called Eddie at six o'clock. It was still dark outside. When Eddie's mother snapped on the light, she said, "It's still snowing. Daddy and Mr. Stewart and Rudy and the twins are all shoveling the snow out of the driveway. Mr. Stewart has to get his car out, because he has to take Sidney and her cello to school. He says he will take you and the twins, too."

"Am I glad!" said Eddie, looking out of the window. "Brother! Is it deep!"

"It's a terrible morning for poor Mr. Saunders and the orchestra," said his mother.

When Eddie's father and brothers came in from clearing the driveway, they were cold and hungry. The boys ate piles of buckwheat cakes with maple syrup and drank big cups of steaming-hot cocoa.

At half-past seven Mr. Stewart blew his horn, and

Eddie and the twins gathered up their things. Eddie had his glockenspiel, and each of his brothers had a trombone.

"I feel sorry for the fellow who has to carry the bass drum this morning," said Mr. Wilson.

"That's Buster Branson," said Eddie. "He plays the drum."

"Poor Buster!" said Mr. Wilson, as the boys departed.

Sidney's father had to drive very slowly, because it was snowing so hard it was difficult to see ahead. When they reached the school, the big orange school buses were parked by the curb at the back of the school. Snow was piled on the roofs of the buses and on the hoods and fenders. It stuck to the windows and windshields.

Mr. Stewart carried Sidney's cello up the steps and inside the school. "Do be careful, Sidney," he said. "When you go out to the bus, don't slip with the cello."

"I'll be careful," said Sidney.

As the children in the orchestra gathered in the hall, Mr. Saunders told them exactly what to do. "Eddie," he said, "be careful with your bells. Sidney, watch out for your cello."

"Sure, Mr. Saunders!" said Eddie. "Sidney, you better be careful you don't take a belly-flopper on your cello."

"We'll go out the back door," said Mr. Saunders. "It will be easier to go down the back path than down the front steps."

Eddie ran to the back door and looked out. "Two men are shoveling the path," he said, "but there's an awful lot of snow out there."

"Remember that you'll be going downhill to the street," said Mr. Saunders. "Take it slowly."

"Where is Spike Lightcap?" said Sidney. "He isn't here."

"His mother is taking him right to the studio," said Mr. Saunders.

"With a box of marshmallows," said Eddie.

Mr. Saunders laughed. "Maybe he will give you one, Eddie," he said.

"Not a chance!" said Eddie.

Now all of the children had arrived, and the time had come to leave for the television station. The men who had been clearing the path had finished. They had moved around to the front of the school.

"Come along!" said Mr. Saunders. "Drum goes first, and take it easy."

The path was narrow and already icy. They went single file, Buster first, carrying the drum; and Eddie behind him. They had not taken more than four steps when Buster's feet slipped out from under him. The drum flew out of his hands and started rolling down the icy path toward the street.

"Hey!" cried Eddie, just as he fell over Buster.

"Oh! Oh!" cried the boys and girls who were standing in the open doorway.

"There goes the drum!" cried Sidney. "There goes the drum!"

While Eddie and Buster were picking themselves up, the drum was rolling along, gathering up snow as it went. Halfway down the hill it ran plumb into a first-grade boy. It knocked him into the deep snow and went on its way. It rolled through the open school-yard gate and out into the street. By this time it was well on the way to becoming a great big snowball.

The members of the orchestra watched with horror. They expected a car to smash the drum as soon as it reached the street, but it rolled on. Eddie and Buster ran after it. So did Mr. Saunders and the two bus drivers.

The drum rolled across the street, into a big snowdrift. It was so heavy with snow that it almost plowed right through the snowdrift. It was exactly as though it had gone in through a door. The three men pulled it out and scraped away the snow. Then Mr. Saunders carried it into one of the buses.

Eddie found the drumsticks in the street. "Good thing I found these," he said to Buster.

Mr. Saunders was relieved when he finally had all of the children in the buses with their instruments. As they started off, he said, "Now if Spike shows up, we're all right."

"He'll show up," said Eddie. "He'll show up for the chocolate-covered marshmallows."

When the orchestra reached the television station, the bus drivers and Mr. Saunders helped the children out of the buses and into the building. The orchestra was taken to a room to wait until it was time to go into the studio. The room was right next to the studio, and the wall between was a glass window. The children could see into the studio, and there was a lot to see. Very few of them had ever been inside a television studio. Spike was the only one who had ever been on a program, and he wasn't there yet.

Eddie had his nose right against the window. He didn't want to miss anything. He could see a beautiful lady standing at the end of a great big room. From a very high ceiling hung huge lamps which made the brightest light Eddie had ever seen. The beautiful lady was standing behind a shiny white kitchen table. Back of her there was a stove and a kitchen sink. She was mixing something in a bowl, but Eddie noticed that she wasn't looking at the bowl. Instead, she was looking straight ahead, talking and smiling just as though somebody were there. While she talked and smiled at nobody, two men moved around her with great big cameras. Another man, on a little truck, raised and lowered a long pole with a microphone on the end. Eddie couldn't hear a thing, but he could see everything. "Mr. Saunders!" he said. "Are we going to give our orchestra concert in that kitchen?"

"It won't be a kitchen when we go in," said Mr. Saunders. "All of the kitchen will be moved away."

Suddenly, down the hall, a child's voice cried out, "Where are my marshmallows?"

"Here comes Spike!" said Eddie.

Then there was a scream. "I won't do it! I won't do it! I won't sing!"

Whoops! thought Eddie. Something has happened to the marshmallows.

Mrs. Lightcap appeared in the door with Spike. "Oh, Mr. Saunders," she said, "a dreadful thing has happened! Mr. Lightcap drove off with the box of marshmallows by mistake."

Spike was yelling now. "I won't sing! I won't sing without the marshmallows."

"L.C.," said his mother, "you are going to sing. I want no more crying over marshmallows."

If they called me Elsie, Eddie thought to himself, I would make them buy me a whole candy store.

Spike went right on yelling.

"Aren't you ashamed, L.C.!" said his mother.

L.C. was not ashamed. He just yelled louder than ever.

"Now, L.C.," said his mother, "I want this nonsense stopped. The marshmallows are safe in Daddy's car. Daddy isn't going to eat your marshmallows. You can have them as soon as you get home."

Mr. Saunders was watching the clock, and Eddie was watching the beautiful lady in the kitchen. Now she was taking a cake out of the oven. It looked good. Eddie hoped they would all get a piece.

"Spike!" said Mr. Saunders. "You'll have to stop crying. We go on in five minutes."

Spike began to quiet down and finally he stopped crying. But now he had the hiccups. His mother went to get a glass of water. When she returned, she handed the glass to Spike and said, "Take ten sips." Spike took ten sips and hiccuped again.

"He should stick his fingers in his ears while he drinks the water," said Rosalie.

Spike stuck his fingers in his ears, and his mother held the glass for him. Most of the water went down the front of his lavender sports jacket and soaked his bow tie. He hiccuped again.

"Put a key down his back," said Buster. "That will stop it sure."

Mrs. Lightcap opened her purse and took out a key.

189

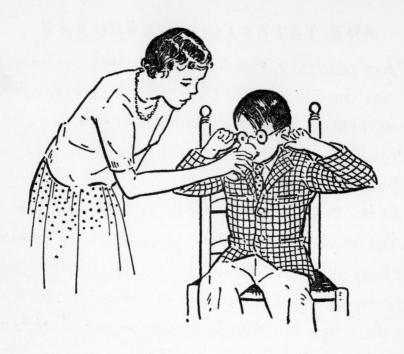

She dropped it inside Spike's shirt collar. Spike hiccuped again and said, "It didn't go inside."

"I know how to stop it," said Frank. Then he whispered to Spike's mother, "I'll scare him. That will fix
it." He went to the door and stepped out into the hall.
He pointed with his finger down the hall. "Oh!" he
cried. "There's a big rat out here!"

Every girl in the orchestra screamed, but the boys
rushed to the door. Spike just hiccuped.

"Are you crazy, Frank?" said his twin brother.

"No!" replied Frank. "I was just trying to scare the hiccups out of Spike, but it didn't work."

Now Mr. Saunders received his signal to take the orchestra into the studio.

At the Wilsons' house, Eddie's mother had turned on the television set. She was pleased to have three of her boys playing in the orchestra, and excited because they were going to be on television. When it came time for the songs, Mr. Saunders made an announcement. "We have had to change our vocalist," he said. "Eddie Wilson, who plays the bells, will now sing three songs."

When Eddie stepped out in front of the orchestra, he remembered the lady who had made the cake in the TV kitchen. He looked right out at nobody, but the whole time he was singing he made believe that he was looking right at his mother's face. And he was! For his mother was looking right at her little boy and feeling very proud of Eddie.